The younger brother Don Yod;
a Tibetan play

THE YOUNGER BROTHER DON YOD

Asian Studies Research Institute

DENIS SINOR, DIRECTOR

ORIENTAL SERIES, NO. 2

THE YOUNGER BROTHER DON YOD

A TIBETAN PLAY TRANSLATED BY

Thubten Jigme Norbu & Robert B. Ekvall

. . . Being the Secret Biography, from the Words of the Glorious Lama, the Holy Reverend Blo bZang Ye SHes

༄༅། །དཔལ་ལྡན་བླ་མ་དམ་པ་རྗེ་བཙུན་བློ་བཟང་ཡེ་ཤེས་ཀྱི་གསུང་ལས་གསང་
བའི་རྣམ་ཐར་བཞུགས་སོ།།

Indiana University Press | *Bloomington & London*
for International Affairs Center

Library of Congress catalog card number: 68-63008

Manufactured in the United States of America

CONTENTS

ILLUSTRATIONS

ALPHABET

Ka	*KHa*	*Ga*	*NGa*	*Ca*	*CHa*	*Ja*	*NYa*
ཀ།	ཁ་	ག་	ང་།	ཅ་	ཆ་	ཇ་	ཉ།

Ta	*THa*	*Da*	*Na*	*Pa*	*PHa*	*Ba*	*Ma*
ཏ་	ཐ་	ད་	ན།	པ་	ཕ་	བ་	མ།

TSa	*TSHa*	*DZa*	*Wa*	*ZHa*	*Za*	*A*	*Ya*
ཙ་	ཚ་	ཛ་	ཝ།	ཞ་	ཟ་	འ་	ཡ།

Ra	*La*	*SHa*	*Sa*	*Ha*	*AH*
ར་	ལ་	ཤ་	ས།	ཧ་	ཨ།

i	*u*	*e*	*o*
ི	ུ	ེ	ོ

ཕྱུར། ... གཅིག

༄། །ཕྱུར་མས་ཞུ་ལ་དགྲོན་ས་མདོ་རྗེས། ཡང་ཕྱུར་དག་ཅིག་སྒྲོན་པ་འི་སྐྲ་ངས་ཞུ་གས་ཀྱི་རྗེ་ལ་ནི་ཞེ་ད་དོ། །དེ་ནས་ཕྱུར་མ་གཅིག་ཞུ་ལ་ང་སྒྲོན་ཏེ།

ཇུ་ན་གཅིག་སྐྱུ་སྐྱུགས་ནས་ལ་དགེ་ལྷ་ཕྱུག་ཀ་བསྐུར་ས། འཕྲུག་ཕྱུར་སྐྱུར་ངོ། །ཕྲན་ནས་ཀ་ཤེག་ཀྱི་ས་པ་ཟན་ཞུ་ལ། ཇི་སྐྱ་ལ་བུ་དེ་ལ་ཡིད་ཕྱི་ཀྱི

ཡ་ཕྱི་ས་ཏུ་ཡེ་ན། ཡ་ལ་ཀ་སྐྱེས། ཕ་དགོ་ཀྱི་ཨ་རྡོ་ཤུག་ས་རྩེ་ཅན། ཧུག །ཕྱོ་ག་ཏེ་ཀྱི་གཟེ་པ་ཡུ་ཕས་ལ་གསུང་ངམ། །ཏེ་ནས་སྒྲོང་གཀས

བདག་ལྷ་འི་དང་ང་ས་ཡི་ཤ་ཀོས་ཀྱི་སྐྱ་ན་རྩེ་ས་པ་དུ་བཞི་དང་ཡིན་ནོ། །

INTRODUCTION

THE Tibetan tale here presented in translation has many titles, but under all of them it remains the same story. The formal title, "Being the Secret Biography of the Words and Deeds of the Glorious Lama, the Holy Reverend *Blo bZang Ye SHes,*" which appears on the first leaf of the Tibetan text, is, however, both pompous and misleading. The story is not a biography of the Holy Reverend Glorious Lama *Blo bZang Ye SHes,* the second Panchen Lama, who held office during the latter part of the seventeenth century. It is a fanciful allegory with a political purpose as precise and pointed as that of any political pamphlet or piece of propaganda. That purpose links the story with the Panchen Lama, who by being assigned the role of narrator is credited with authorship. Therefore, the story does in a sense become his story.

A widely known folktale and one of the most popular plays in the repertoire of wandering theatrical troupes, it is known to the Tibetan public by a variety of names, such as *rGyal Po Don Yod (King Don Yod), Don Yod Don aGrub rNam THar (The Don Yod Don aGrub Biography), gCung Po Don Yod Don aGrub sGrung (The Younger Brother Don Yod and Don aGrub Tale), Don Yod Don aGrub (Don Yod and Don aGrub), gCung Po Don Yod (The Younger Brother Don Yod),* and *Don CHung Don CHen (Little Don, Big Don).* All of these titles have one thing in common that is of considerable significance: *Don Yod,* the name of the younger brother, is, in each instance, mentioned first. The story is thus popularly accepted as that of the younger brother. *gCung Po Don Yod (The Younger Brother Don Yod),* one of the most frequently used and apt of these designations, has been selected as the title under which this story is introduced to the English reader.

The story is essentially drama. Although given a third-person narrative form that, because of the complexities of typology and the implications of the doctrine and accepted fact of rebirth, has at times the overtones of first-person narrative, the scenes, the entrances and exits, the characters, the speeches and the songs of a dramatic production appear very clearly. The strict format of drama is not known in Tibetan literature, yet frequently the text of this story suggests the cue sheets of a prompter in the wings.

This is quite in accord with its place in Tibetan folklore. It is, indeed, one of a half dozen popular dramas which are played—particularly in the fall and New Year festivals—all over Tibet. Four of the six, in whole or in part, have been translated into English (H. I. Woolf, 1924; M. H. Duncan, 1955), but Don Yod has not previously appeared in English. Relatively few Tibetans have read the text that follows the long formal title, and many fail to identify that title with the play that they have seen and listened to since infancy. There are few, however, who do not know the play and who cannot identify the principal parts. When the strolling players arrive in a community to play, sing, and dance *Don Yod,* all the members of that community become their audience, and some even become drama critics, knowing to a nicety how the lines should be said or the arias sung.

In the degree to which the wardrobe resources of the troupe permit, the actors are dressed for their parts: kings, princes, beggars, monks, etc., wearing costumes which are sometimes elaborate but always at least allusive. The spirit beings, Nagas, animals, birds, and reptiles wear appropriate masks and wings, furry coats, feathers, tails, etc.

The play is seldom, if ever, acted on a stage. It is usually presented in a courtyard or in a communal gathering place such as a village square, a threshing floor, or some similar open space. Thus there is no such thing as up- or downstage. The audience surrounds the players, much as the crowds attending the *sMon Lam CHen Mo* (great wish-prayer) on the 13th of the First Moon form a compact ring around that dramatic and allegorical dance. Stage props are minimal or non-existent.

There are those who hold that a correct presentation of the play should, in action, speeches, and songs, closely follow the text of the story; but much improvisation and elaboration does take place. This is especially true with regard to the songs, of which there are only five in the recorded script, all moralistic in tone and doctrinal in content—more like hymns than songs. These five are always sung or chanted in a style reminiscent of a liturgical service.

In addition to these songs, there has evolved from the action and scenes of the play a collection of folksongs with such themes as "The Two Brothers Wander in Exile," "The Death of *Don Yod,*" "The Resurrection of *Don Yod,*" "The Descent into Nagaland," etc. Although these are sometimes included in the presentation of the play, they also have an independent existence as lullabies and as important items in the repertoires of wandering minstrels.

Some of the action, such as the performance of circumambulation, the making of salutations, and activities common to gatherings and festivals, is rhythmically interpreted in dancing and stylized gesturing and posturing to the beat of drums and other percussion instruments. Occasionally stringed instruments are used to accompany the singing of the songs. Much of the play depends on effective recitative carrying the thread of the story and introducing what takes place, against which the players act and speak their parts.

The story has two separate and distinct themes: one the consciously planned and purposed theme, which is enunciated from the beginning, and the other a warmly emotional one which appears to unfold without plan and in seeming disregard of the heavily stressed "message" of the drama. The former theme is political in character and is concerned with intrigue and struggle for power, but its development relies heavily on religious concepts and sanctions. The latter is a folk theme of fraternal love between half brothers and gains much of its importance from its widespread acceptance. The numerous titles previously cited illustrate the popularity of this emotional theme.

The religio-political theme had its genesis in the rivalry between *gTSang,* the west central province of Tibet which was the seat of the Panchen Lama's power and influence, and the province of *dBus* where the Dalai Lama had just consolidated a "central authority" in Lhasa; and in the immediate struggle between supporters of the Panchen Lama and those of the Dalai Lama. The exercise of temporal power over all of Tibet, a power bestowed on the Dalai Lama by Gushri Khan in 1642, and the ecclesiastical superiority of the Dalai Lama over the Panchen Lama were highly distasteful to the *gTSang* faction.

In the context of this power struggle, the theme of the play is revealed as an attempt to establish the priority, in doctrinal precedence, of the Panchen Lama. He is the "Lord Light Unmeasured," and one of the Buddhas; the Dalai Lama is only the "son of his mind," the Bodhisattva "Viewing Eye." In typology the Panchen Lama is the teacher and preceptor and the Dalai Lama is the pupil and disciple: the Panchen Lama is the benefactor and the Dalai Lama is the one benefited. Throughout the play these and similar distinctions are overtly emphasized and subtly suggested.

The resentment of the Panchen Lama and his faction quite naturally is focused on and directed against the Dalai Lama's prime minister, who is made the villain—in deepest hue—of the play. In the preliminary remarks he is introduced as heretic and unbeliever. He is shown as being equally the enemy of the prototype of the Dalai Lama, plotting his destruction, and the enemy of the prototype of the Panchen Lama, seeking to disrupt his plans and completely discredit him. He is presented as an unrepentant ingrate who, though forgiven and rewarded, persists in seeking, by intrigue, treachery, and armed rebellion, the overthrow of his generous and compassionate superiors. Of all the living creatures—human and nonhuman—in the play, his is the only death which is final—a death unmitigated by restoration to life or the gracious promise of favorable rebirth. His end is violent—in the crash and roar of an avalanche.

Not much is known of the real-life prime minister of the Dalai Lama, against whom this animosity is directed and consistently maintained.

During the spring of 1674, when the story allegedly was told, the actual prime minister of the Dalai Lama was *Blo bZang mTHu sTobs,* who had previously been in charge of offerings and who had been made prime minister in 1669. In the spring of 1675—one year after the story was promulgated—he was removed from office for scandalous involvement with a Saskyapa lady of rank who was a nun. He must have had many powerful friends among the officials and clergy, for, although the attempt to exonerate him was abandoned, so much influence was exerted on his behalf that he was granted a special title as ex-minister and given the fief of *Zangs Ri.* Before he left Lhasa early in the spring of 1676, he was officially honored by the Mongol Khan, who was, in a sense, the final court of appeal and source of power in the Tibetan capital.

There is no way of knowing whether the promulgation of the story, in which the prime minister is pre-figured as villain, played any part in bringing about his disgrace, but it is safe to assume that the clique of the Panchen Lama felt that he was vulnerable and therefore focused their attack on him, hoping to bring discredit upon the party and policies of the Dalai Lama.

In contrast to this insistent and purposeful enunciation of a motif, which at times becomes sheer propaganda, the theme of brother love unfolds with little emphasis but with strong and moving appeal. The two are half brothers with seven years difference in age, and the ambitiously jealous mother of the younger one is the elder's hateful stepmother, who plots his death and would like nothing better than to have his heart served to her on a platter. Between the brothers, however, all is tender affection. They share everything. With scant regard for his own mother, the younger brother clings to the elder and follows him into exile to meet death from hunger and thirst. The elder cares unselfishly for the younger, depriving himself of food, and seeking vainly, by body heat and the moisture of his own saliva, to prolong the life of his brother. Later, newly married to a passionate princess and having just come into a kingdom, he leaves both to return to the spot where in desparation he had made a temporary tomb for the younger brother, seeking either his bones or assurance that he is still alive. There the brothers are united, for the younger has been restored to life by emanations of Brahma and Indra. In great pomp they share the two kingdoms and the same wife.

The institution of polyandrous marriage to brothers, well authenticated in parts of Tibet, suggests that fraternal loyalty and affection is a theme of special significance and acceptability to Tibetans. In Tibet there are no fixed rights of inheritance and brothers usually either share in joint ownership or equally divide family inheritance. Brotherly affection and loyalty are, on the whole, strong and, although the extended family tends to break up rather easily into nuclear families, even after such a break-up good relationships and patterns of close cooperation and mutual aid between brothers and their families are maintained. When an extended family does not break up in this manner, much of its cohesiveness derives from economic considerations. However, a high degree of brotherly regard and a strong sense of community rights are needed to overcome natural sexual jealousy and make it feasible for a younger brother to share conjugal privilege as he reaches sexual maturity. Such an arrangement may be a temporary one, or it may develop into a permanent polyandrous marriage.

In the story, rights of succession based on primogeniture are made the subject of much discussion and theatrical by-play, but they are rejected in the final solution; for the younger brother is the one who succeeds to the throne of his ancestors. The elder, on the other hand, is granted only the throne and kingly power of his father-in-law. This arrangement, whereby the rights of succession and inheritance are acquired by a son-in-law, is also very common in Tibet.

The emergence of these and other conflicting concepts and divergent viewpoints in the development of the story are part of a more fundamental and pervasive dichotomy. There is a general, and at times confusing, tendency to mix Tibetan and Indic concepts, mythology, situations, environments and even names.

At the outset it is flatly stated that the locale and setting of the story are in India, although the place is given a Tibetan name. The first action has to do with the seashore, elephants, boats, and a voyage over the ocean to a land beyond the sea—all of which are foreign to Tibet. The spirit beings to whom prayers must be said and offerings made include pre-Buddhistic Indian deities, members of the Buddhist pantheon from the Jewel on down, and "locality owners" of Tibetan origin. Typically Tibetan sports are engaged in and Tibetan "victory beer" is quaffed by the multiracial crowd of an Indian city. The princes go into exile with an elephant and mounts—presumably horses—but eventually arrive on foot in the uninhabited *Byang THang* (Northern Plain), which is the specific geographic name for the high central plateau of Tibet, where however, the story's flora and fauna are a bizarre mixture of those of the austere Tibetan uplands and the lush jungles of India. Persimmon trees bear fruit, sandalwood grows, and parrots talk where the Tibetan steppe partridge wanders.

In the matter of names there is complete confusion. Most of the Nagas—important in Indic mythology—are listed by Tibetan names. The first of the dramatis personae, however, who comes on stage is a king with an Indian name. His first wife, who is the daughter of another king with an Indian name, has a Tibetan name. His second wife, a woman of the common people, also has a Tibetan name. His two sons, the princes, who are two of the three principal characters of the play, have Tibetan names. Of the two "pious ministers" of this king, the one first mentioned has a Tibetan name. The bride-princess, heroine of the story, is designated by a Tibetan title and name, but her father has an Indian name which is later changed to a Tibetan one when he becomes a monk. The villain of the story in both his roles is known by an Indian name.

There is perhaps some logic in the prevalence of Tibetan names. The half dozen or so Tibetan plays of this genre, of which some are "birth stories of the Buddha," are classified by some Tibetan scholars in accordance with how much or how little Indian influence is apparent in their style or content.* *gCung Po Don Yod (The Younger Brother Don Yod)* is reckoned to be a "birth story." The situation underlying the allegory and the theme of fraternal love is traditionally Tibetan, although, as befits a "birth story," it is located in India and has acquired Indian trappings and names (which, however, tend to become meaningless in the context of the story). For example, the lake near the palace of King Gocha into which the dragon had plunged and through which the prince made his sacrificial descent into the watery realm of the Nagas, is commonly believed to be the pool behind the Potala in Lhasa. So stories change, sometimes as much in the hearing as in the telling.

The Tibetan text from which this translation has been made is a reasonably clear xylograph printed on thin Tibetan paper from blocks whose size averages approximately 2″ x 11″. There are forty-four folios printed on both sides with six lines on each side; the number of letters in a line varies from sixty to seventy. In addition, there are four lines on one face of an additional folio. There is no

* The most famous of these, known in Tibetan as *Dri Med Kun lDan,* but more widely by its Sanskrit title *Vishvantara,* seems to be entirely Indian in origin and concept, although when adapted and recited from memory by wandering Tibetan minstrels, it acquires a Tibetan setting and Tibetan characteristics. *sNang gSal* (Clear Light), a play about the piety of a Tibetan maiden, which Bacot has said has "un charactère avancé et subtil," is apparently purely Tibetan in theme and form, but it is not a "birth story."

proper colophon. Attribution of authorship is thus only inferential, and no indication is given as to when or where the xylograph was printed.

The style, except where formalized and trite doctrinal utterances are introduced, is colloquial, with many of the contractions and idioms (in disregard of the niceties of grammar) characteristic of free oral discourse. This colloquial tendency shows up strongly in the frequent use of the genitive particle in all its forms (Gi, Gyi, and Kyi) for the instrumental (Gis, Gyis, and Kyis). Indeed, it is explicitly stated at the end that the story has been told in conversational style, like the telling of the Gesar epic.

The long history of this translation is inextricably involved with recent Tibetan history. In 1951, when the Communist Chinese began their conquest of Tibet, Mr. Norbu, as Abbot of the monastery of Kumbum, became their virtual prisoner. After an arduous and hazardous flight from China to Lhasa and on to the United States, he spent a period of enforced rest at the home of Robert Ekvall, an American who, having spent a good part of his life in Tibet, is fluent in the Tibetan language. During this period Mr. Norbu and Mr. Ekvall collaborated on a rough translation of this characteristic and inherently interesting play.

Years of divergent and intense activity intervened for both of them after Mr. Norbu regained his health. Then in 1961 Mr. Norbu joined the Tibetan Research Project just beginning at the University of Washington. There, with the help of a number of native Tibetan scholars who had come to the University on Rockefeller grants to join the Project, the translation of the Tibetan text was carefully revised and the extensive explanations and supplementary information compiled which have been recorded in the notes.

Two of the native Tibetan scholars—Dachen Rinpoche, the titular head of the Sakya sect, and Dezhung Rinpoche, the learned tutor and preceptor of the Sakya family—went over the Tibetan text phrase by phrase and line by line in a search with the translators for the true meaning of meaning, and for the tradition and behavior patterns in the history and culture of the Tibetans that underlie such meaning. The four men, representing three different areas of Tibet and four distinctly different viewpoints, participated in these long sessions of free discussion and argument. Special deference must be paid to Dezhung Rinpoche and his views concerning certain areas of Tibetan scholarship. In most matters a consensus was eventually achieved; when there was no consensus, the differences were usually regional. To a considerable degree, the notes reflect the consensus.

The Tibetan spelling of Tibetan words is used in the English text, with the exception of certain anglicized spellings of such well-known names as Lhasa and the Potala, and such words as "lama." The Indic names in the Tibetan text are transliterated in the widely followed convention for transcribing Sanskrit, i. e., Deva for De Wa, etc.

The Tibetan text, printed from woodblocks and undated, was edited for typographical errors, principally by Dezhung Rinpoche, before the translation was made. The Tibetan script in the present edition was copied from the edited text by Rev. Cho-gyatso of the First Kalmyk Temple at Farmingdale, New Jersey. The illustrator, Mr. Legshad, is a Tibetan artist living in India.

In addition to the participants in the specific and detailed discussions of the play to whom this translation owes so much, we are indebted to the other Tibetans then in Seattle who contributed descriptions of actors they had seen play "King Don Yod," as well as to the many unnamed players and minstrels on the Tibetan plateau who through the centuries have told and sung the story of Don Yod.

Our thanks go also to others much nearer in time and place: the members of the Inner Asia Colloquium who, under the leadership of Dr. Li Fang-kuei, by stimulating argument and suggestion helped to keep us at our task and to encourage its completion.

Finally, we are grateful for the funds from the Rockefeller and Carnegie foundations, which brought us and the other Tibetan scholars together in the Far Eastern Institute of the University of Washington and gave us the time in which to do the work, and to the Ford Foundation which, through the Indiana University International Affairs Center and the Asian Studies Research Institute made possible the publication of this volume.

To all these and all others who have helped us, we dedicate this book, the result of our efforts.

THE TRANSLATORS

THE YOUNGER BROTHER DON YOD

NOTE Marginal numbers refer to the corresponding pages of Tibetan text

THE YOUNGER BROTHER DON YOD

ON THE high day of the moon of *Sa Ga* in the Wood Male Tiger Year[1] the most holy glorious lama himself grasps the thunderbolt. The Perfect One, the emanation-body of the All-Knowing Panchen,[2] being twelve years of age, while in the private room of the lama's residence holds the doctrine with a joyous mind. The Great Wizard in the Presence[3] and I—official-pupil[4]—the two of us respectfully sought guidance, saying: f 1

"The one of high position[5] has no liking for us—official-pupil—of this our *bKra SHis lHun Po.* Therefore the subsidy from the place of central authority has already been reduced. But the original All-Knowing One's lotus feet remain firm,[6] and whatever dissension and occasion for harm can arise to the Victorious One,[7] father-son they are. The one of high position is very severe. When there is no way of knowing the purposes of the central authority, our duties will not prosper nor will we eat in peace. With foreboding I am saying this."

Eyes closed for a moment, he was sitting still; then, smiling slightly, he spoke. "If the prime minister is able, many losses do not come and our fame does not suffer. His Holiness, the Victorious One, ten thousand years ago was King *Don THams Cad aGrub Pa,* and at the time this prime minister was born as *Trishu,* the minister of King *Gocha.* When we at that time became the lama, the minister believed a heresy, and the force of this heretical belief prevented him from having faith in us." f 2

"Such being the case, what is the story?" we questioned.

"That which I remember I tell in its order." So he spoke.

"Now make saluations to the sublime one of great mercy. I will explain the secret record of the history and life story of the pious King *Don THams Cad aGrub Pa.*

"In the sublime land of India, in a place called *gTogs Pa Zangs Gling,* it is said there was a pious king, *Bhala Deva.* To him as wife was *Kun bZang Ma,*[8] the daughter of King *Shari Bhadra.* Several years passed and she had not yet borne a son.

"The female diviner named *Karna* practiced divination, saying: 'If you will go beyond the outer ocean and make offerings and pray to the gods and Nagas of *Kosha,* a son will come.' Such was the prophecy.

" 'If a son is born, I will bestow thanksgiving gifts upon you,' he promised.

"Then the king—father-mother—the ministers and subjects, in number roughly one thousand, adorned according to custom, loaded the required things for the offerings intended for the gods and Nagas on many elephants and went to the ocean beach. In boats and ships they then sailed the surface of the sea for five days.

"Arriving at the place—the pure land of *Kosha* where dwell the gods, Nagas and land-owners[9]—for seven days they prayed to the Rare Perfection[10] and presented heaped-up oblations to the god *TSa Muntri*[11] and the protectors of religion. They also presented f 3 displayed offerings and oblations[12] to the eight classes of aboriginal beings.[13]

"On the night of the seventh day, in a dream, the king saw a white *AH TSa Ra,*[14] wearing a crystal rosary, who approached him and said, 'Two princes will be born, both sons of my mind, the emanations of *sPyan Ras gZigs* and *aJam dPal.* Rejoice.'

" 'Who are you?' questioned the king.

" 'I am Lord *Od dPag Med*[15] of the western heaven of bliss,' he said. '*TSa Muntri,* the lord of the land of *Kosha,* also is your protector. He is the protector of you three—father-sons—in your many births. You should repeatedly make offerings and oblations to the protector.'

" 'This good dream is also a sign of the coming of sons,' the king said.

"The auspices being favorable, he went to his palace.

"Nine or ten months later in the Tiger Year a son was begotten in the womb of *Kun bZang Ma.* At this event flowers came down like rain. A rainbow like a tent of light and similar auspicious signs appeared again and again. At good times[16] the unusual sight of a white-robed goddess, coming from the sky and showering the queen with water, was clearly seen by all.

"The months and days having passed, a unique and marvelous son, having the auspicious marks and the letter *'Hri'* luminously manifest on his chest, was born. The subjects of the king then gathered in a great birth festival. Offerings of thanksgiving were made to the Rare Perfection, to the gods of the country, and to the protectors of religion. f 4

"The child being shown to *Bhadra,* the sign-discerning[17] Brahmin, he said, 'With signs and beauty adorned amazingly, it looks as if he is the emanation of *Lo Ke SHwa Ri* (Avalokitesvara). Before the king has passed on, this most excellent one will come to take the place of a king.[18] Is this the hope of our possible happiness?'

"Then the king—father-mother—the two, the subjects, the courtiers, and the servants all rejoiced. Trumpets were sounded; banners were unfurled; and music was played. The child was named King *Don THams Cad aGrub Pa,*[19] and many presents were given to the two: the female diviner and *Bhadra* the discerner of signs.

"Furthermore, the female diviner was appointed minister.

"From that time on, the law of the land developed in accordance with the teachings of the doctrine.

"When King *Don THams Cad aGrub Pa* was five years old, the six letters,[20] they alone, were on his lips. It was a time of marvels.

"*Kun bZang Ma* then became very ill and died.

"Everyone said, 'The life sap of the land is diminished,' and wept. The greatest of all funeral ceremonies was performed.

"When about a year had passed, the ministers and the people took counsel, saying, 'Although a lady like her is not to be found on earth, yet the king, being still young, should look for a wife.' Concerning this all were agreed.

"For several months the ministers looked for such a lady but could not find a suitable one. In this period, however, a great ceremonial offering was celebrated in the land. The king—father-son—the two, were invited. Among all the women gathered in the crowd there was a girl of the common people, called *Padma Can,* who, having the beauty of youth, was seen by the king. f 5

"The king then secretly gave orders and sent a minister. On the following day the king-father went to bathe in the pool of the garden. Just at that time *Radari,* the minister of affairs within, brought *Padma Can* to the king, who was pleased. Without any marriage ceremony the king just took her, as a matter of course, into the palace.

"Behind the king's back, however, the people criticized him, saying, 'He has taken an unworthy[21] lady.'

"Then, in a dream the girl *Padma Can* saw an ascetic with brown hair, wearing a garment of yellow cotton cloth, and holding a wheel in his hand, who said, 'I am the son of Lord *Od dPag Med.* Lend me a place to stay.' He was then merged into her forehead.

"She told this to the father.

"He said, 'In the land of *Kosha* it also was prophesied that there will be two CHANG CHUB SEMPA[22] emanations. Make yourself clean of contamination.'

"The months and days coming to an end, there was born to the unworthy lady a marvelous and glorious son.

"To celebrate the birth a very great offering was made to the Rare Perfection and to the protectors of religion.

"*Bhadra,* the Brahmin, was invited and was shown the child.

f 6 " 'Without doubt this is also an emanation of a CHANG CHUB SEMPA. Give the youth the name *Don Yod.*'[23]

"Instantly it rained flowers, the earth moved, and all the propitious signs were manifested. On the palms of the prince's hands and on the soles of his feet the wheel was unmistakably outlined, giving forth light.

"Following his birth he was breast-fed by his mother, but he had no desire to be with her or the nurse. Instead he went to be with his elder brother, Prince *Don THams Cad aGrub Pa,* and remained at his side day and night. Young though this son was, he very much preferred to be with his brother. They shared their food, and when they slept they shared the same bed, bed covers, and pillow.

"When the two sons were still young, they once went up on the palace roof to look around.

"On several days the lady also went up on the palace roof. On one of these days she looked eastward through an opening in the parapet and saw to the east tens of thousands of pleasure seekers who, as they idled, gossiped and spoke maliciously.

"Among them were several nobles who consulted together saying, 'To this our own great king are born two sons. It is proper that the elder prince should be appointed to the place of the king. Because of the mother it is not proper that the younger one should.'[24]

"Others there were who said, 'The mother of this same Prince *Don aGrub* was a king's daughter. *Don aGrub* himself has the signs and marks of a Buddha. It is proper that he should be in the place of the king. Prince *Don Yod* has many wonderful signs and marks, and between the two brothers there is no great difference, but because his mother is unworthy and he is the younger, he cannot get the place of the king.' f 7

"Hearing this talk, the lady became somewhat displeased in her mind.

"Then she looked southward from the roof of the palace toward a great plain where the men were all competing in archery, jumping, and the lifting of stones. When the sport ended, they drank victory beer and shouted, 'King *Don aGrub* will be our king. King *Don Yod* is, moreover, the younger brother and therefore cannot get the place of the king.' What they said resembled what had been said earlier.

"Because of this the lady thought, 'It appears that my son will not get the place of the king. It seems that the people speak badly of him.' Thinking this, she was displeased.

"Again from the roof of the palace she looked westward and saw women who all appeared to be weaving and stretching the warp. During the forenoon they were spinning silk floss, and during the afternoon they were talking much among themselves. The women were of a different class; their pale foreheads were clearly visible as they talked, saying:

" 'Our Prince *Don THams Cad aGrub Pa* is the eldest son. As his mother is also a king's daughter, he will get the king's throne. The mother of Prince *Don Yod,* however, is an unworthy one. Also he is the younger; he cannot get the place of the king.' f 8

"At this the lady did not have a moment of peace in her mind.

"Looking northward from the palace, she saw in all about a

thousand boys and girls playing together. Some of the boys made a throne of adobe bricks and said, 'Prince *Don aGrub* will be appointed to the place of the king.'

"One boy sat on this and said, 'I am King *Don THams Cad aGrub Pa.*'

"Many of the children pretended they were requesting audience of the king and said, 'We are ministers of King *Don aGrub.*'

"Others said, 'We are subjects,' and taking off their clothes held them by the edges and dragged them on the ground saying, 'These are hand-gifts.'[25]

"Another said, 'I am King *Don Yod,*' and putting a rug at the base of the throne, sat on it.

"The auspices were in accord that Prince *Don THams aGrub Pa* would gain the place of the king. Having heard this, all the ministers, young and old, men and women, also were in accord and decided to designate Prince *Don aGrub* as king. All the people, agreeing, voiced approval.

"But the lady kept thinking, 'Although Prince *Don THams aGrub Pa* has no mother, he himself[26] has a good name, these auspices, and popular acclaim,[27] and is favored in the talk and attitudes of the ministers. From these things I can see that the elder will seize the place of the king. My son, it appears, will not gain that place. Should my son not win, I, his mother, will be of no account; therefore I should seek an occasion to do away with this prince.' Such were her malicious thoughts.

f 9 "Then she put red ochre inside her right cheek and indigo inside her left cheek so that what she coughed up had streaks of red and blue. Having eaten the *Sug Pa* herb[28] and elephant brains, she vomited and sneezed violently. Then going down the stairs to the area surrounding the palace, to where the king—father-son—were circumambulating the shrine of the 'body, word, and mind,'[29] she fell down on the circumambulation path, coughed up blue and red phlegm, discoloring the ground, and as she coughed cried out, *'AHa Hu KHyu!'*

"The king asked, 'What is your sickness?'

"Other than saying, 'I am sick,' she would say nothing.

"The great pious king, because the first lady had died, now wondered frantically, 'What is the best thing to do?'

"Then the female diviner performed divination, and the astrologer cast the horoscope to no good; and ritual offerings of proper food and great efficacy were made, but also to no advantage.

"After that, the female diviner, being clairvoyant, said, 'The great queen consort is neither really sick nor are the bones and skin affected. The sickness comes of much worry and vexation.'

"The king himself was beginning, however, to be sick from anxiety. After three days he decided it was best to question the lady herself about her condition, and he went to the girl *Padma Can.*

" 'Do you yourself have anything to say about what would benefit your illness? If you have, it will be done,' he said.

"The lady then said, 'There is something which would benefit me; however, it cannot be done. I myself will die. Leave me alone.' f 10

"The king then said, 'All right, whatever it is that will benefit you will be done.'

"The lady said, 'If I tell you what will benefit me, you must first take an oath that whatever it may be, it will be done.'

"Thereupon, before the shrine, the king took the oath.

"After that the lady said, 'Before this I thought that the great king would never be able to offer any such possibility of help, so I did not tell you. This one, our king, *Don THams Cad aGrub Pa,* is the magical manifestation of a non-human demon. When he was born, his mother, *Kun bZang Ma,* who was regarded as worthy by all, died. Now he works harm to cause me to die. As for myself, that is a small matter; but from prophecies and dreams received, I know that the life of the king is in danger from him. If he [the boy] is killed and his heart is given to me, it will benefit me, and the demon who would harm the life of the king will have been removed. Should this be not done, if he is then taken across the outer ocean, to the uninhabited shores of *Kosha,* all still will be well.' Thus she spoke.

"The king father thought, 'At the time my wife, the incomparable one, was living, because prayers were made to the Rare Perfection and offerings and oblations were made to guardians of the Word and the protectors of religion, this son was given. The Brahmin astrologer prophesied that before I died this child would take the place of a king. If my royal place is not the one taken, there is no possibility of getting the place of any other king. The female diviner, however, was prophesying about a demon. How can it be that this anguish has come—and to me? Is this reality or a dream?' f 11

"Thinking thus, the king said, 'Even to benefit your sickness, it is not right to kill this son, *Don THams Cad aGrub Pa,* because it is forbidden to harm sentient beings. Great misfortune comes. When dead, they are reborn in the hell of torment. We will not act in this manner. However, what you suggest about sending him into exile—well, that might be all right.'

"Thus words rashly spoken became his acceptance.

"The lady, as she heard the words of the king, began to improve slightly.

"The king then collected the people and spoke, 'Our prince *Don THams Cad aGrub Pa* is indeed the emanation of a demon, but it is not right to kill him. He himself, in the first instance, was begged from the gods; yet he must be sent away from this country. Prepare the determination of the auspices and the needed equipment for his going.'

"Once the King had spoken,[30] there was no answer the ministers could make.

"Nevertheless, among themselves, they spoke in the strongest terms against the king, saying, 'If Prince *Don THams Cad aGrub Pa* is exiled, our realm will break up, and all because of this lady's word.' All the people also were displeased.

f 12 "After this, those favoring Prince *Don aGrub* said to him, 'This our queen hates you with passion and with much evil counsel is urging the king to kill the prince!'

"The prince then thought, 'Better to flee than be killed. I will flee.'

"The two brothers, however, continued to occupy the same sleeping quarters, and there they collected and hid whatever leftover food there was.

"At that time someone sent from the father-mother came to Prince *Don Yod* and said, 'Your small clothes, small shoes, and small arrows no longer fit you. Come and try some others.'

"Though the messenger invited him, yet the two brothers were so attached to each other that he would not go to the king—father-mother.

"After this King *Don THams Cad aGrub Pa* said to his own younger brother, 'The people are about to send me, your elder brother, into exile. The father-mother so ordered. It is not good for you to remain with your elder brother.'

"Then *Don Yod,* the younger brother, said, 'If you, elder brother, are going to be exiled, take me with you as elder brother's companion.' As he said this he put his arms around the elder brother's neck.

"To this the elder brother said, 'On the way to exile there is nothing good; food and drink will be scarce, there will be many dangers, and I will be thrown into the great outer ocean.[31] You yourself must not suffer such a fate, but must take care of the family inheritance and fill well the place of the king. The mother will have no other son. If both of us are thrown into the water, the royal line will be cut off. Instead, you yourself should stay on in the ancestral home. For my part I must not disobey the order of the father-mother, and must fulfill their purpose. Even if I am killed, I will then not regret it.' f 13

"Prince *Don Yod* wept and said to the elder brother, 'Such suffering happening to you, elder brother, means the end of the royal line. Dead or alive we two are together.

"He refused to move one step from the elder.

"The king—father-mother—ordered, 'Since Prince *Don aGrub* will be exiled tomorrow, you, the ministers, take care not to lose him. Bring the younger brother *Don Yod* inside.'

"Reckoning the planets and stars, the time was adjudged to be propitious, and the plans to exile him were completed.

"Prince *Don aGrub* then thought, 'I cannot leave my younger brother, yet if the two of us go together and my younger brother is no longer here, the king—father-mother—will fall sick from anxiety. If by mutual agreement the two of us die, the royal line will be cut off.'

"Thinking thus, he got up quickly at midnight, but the younger brother heard him and, putting his arms around his brother's neck, pulled him down and said, 'If you elder brother go, take me with you.'

"So that night he was unable to leave.

"At that time the elder brother was thirteen years[32] old and the younger brother was six. The former, continuing to look for an opportunity to leave, took the food which had been collected and which was kept at his pillow, and put it in a leather bag. Thus for several nights the elder brother tried to leave, but each time the younger one became aware of it and he was unable to go. f 14

" 'No matter what happens he is not willing to stay,' he thought.

"On Thursday, the day of the conjunction of the planet Jupiter and the eighth lunar mansion, when everyone—great and small—was asleep, he took the leather bag and started.

"The younger brother, because of worry over his elder brother's going, had neither undressed nor taken off his shoes, so he arose and went after his elder brother, sobbing and saying, 'Where you go I will go.'

"Thus they went away.

"Then the elder brother said, 'Child, in this manner you yourself buy your own suffering. What a pity that in addition to the suffering of the elder brother you the younger brother also must suffer.'

"Saying this, he took him along.

"When the two pious ministers, *Rab brTan* and *Dzaya Dhara,*[33] heard of this they said farewell to the brother princes and, without letting the father-mother hear about it, they provided riding animals, a loaded elephant, and also attendants to escort them the distance of half a month's journey. The two ministers also sowed earnest wish-prayers[34] for the prince brothers' onward journey.

"When they had traveled over several roads for half a month, all but three of the attendants returned. Those however were unwilling to go back and wept in their anguish of mind.

f 15

"Then Prince *Don aGrub* said:

'To each of the six classes of sentient beings[35] comes his own retribution.
'Companionship followed by separation is natural law.[36]
'Gathering together is not forever but like guests who assemble.
'This life is not forever but like summer clouds.
'As to wealth itself, it is not forever but like merchants' goods.
'Contemplation of the "not forever"—this the essence of great religion.
'Now you may return yonder, praying that hereafter ministers and people meet.'

"Yet the three did not go back.

"Again he spoke:

'Phenomena do not last forever—they are destroyed.
'Youth does not last forever—like the rainbow in the sky.
'The illusory body does not last forever—like the summer flower.
'The end of being born is to die—this is the basic principle of nature.
"I say to all return yonder—pray we meet in the Buddha field.'

"When he had said this, they returned.

"The riding animals and the elephant were sold, one by one, in the inhabited region; and they then went on farther for about fifty leagues[37] to the pathless sandy Northern Plain[38] where there were no longer any dwellings of men.

The younger brother becoming tired there, the elder brother took his hand to lead him; and, eating the remaining food, they went on.

"In the meantime the king—father-mother—arose in the morning, and, the arrangements for sending the prince into exile having been completed, they sent someone to call the prince. f 16

" 'The two brother princes are not to be seen,' the messenger reported to the king.

" 'That is impossible. They must be somewhere in the area—among our own subjects. Go and look for them.'

"The ministers searched among the people but did not find them. Then the king—father-mother—became very anxious, and the lady indeed, without feigning, came to know real illness. Also, the subjects of the king all wept because of the misfortune experienced by the two prince brothers.

"There were many who said as with one voice, 'It is proper and fitting that this should come upon the queen.'

"In the meantime the two prince brothers went on several leagues into the Northern Plain and arrived at a place where neither the voice of men nor the barking of dogs was to be heard—where many rock demons, goblins, and fearful beasts of prey were gathered.

"Because of the compassion of Prince *Don THams Cad aGrub Pa*—CHANG CHUB SEMPA—the rock demons, goblins, and beasts of prey did not harm the two brothers.

"For several months they remained in the uninhabited Northern

Plain. Each day the elder brother ate only a morsel, but without fail gave a spoonful of food to the younger brother. The days having passed, what they had was finished.

"Then they wondered, 'What shall we do?'

"After that, they cut the leather bag into pieces and, eating it, went on; but because the bag was salty they experienced extreme burning thirst. So as they went farther and farther into the Northern Plain, the strength of their bodies lessened.

f 17

"At that point they rested, sitting in the shade of a tree, and the elder brother, seeing there were many persimmons, was conscious of encouragement. After they had picked a great quantity of the fruit, the two of them ate and were refreshed, as wilted flowers are revived when watered.

"Prince *Don THams Cad aGrub Pa* then took five of the fruit in his hands and, presenting an offering, sowed this manner of wish-prayer: 'To you, lamas, guardian deities, Rare-Perfect-Three, sky creatures, protectors of religion, gods of the country, and land-owners, a clean offering-oblation is made. Be pleased to partake of this and be the savior lords of us two. Heedless of obstacles and physical suffering, we have promised to obey the word of the father-mother. We two, in the time of decadence and testing, will be savior lords, destined to draw toward liberation the six classes of sentient beings.'

"They went on for two days to a region where there was no water. From there on, the younger brother could no longer walk; but the elder brother carried him on his back for a distance of about four miles but still could find no water.

"There was a hill[39] like an elephant's nose, and he wondered, 'Is there water behind it?'

f 18

" 'You yourself stay here and I the elder brother will go and look for water,' he said.

"At this statement the younger brother said, 'Elder brother, are you about to abandon me?'

"The prince answered, 'How could I abandon you? But if water is not produced, we both die. It is best to go and look for water.'

"So he went on, but when he had gone about the distance of an earshot there still was no water. As he arrived at the brow of the hill, the elder brother kept looking back to where the younger brother was craning his neck to keep him in sight.

" 'Elder brother!' he cried loudly.

"The elder brother stopped and, looking back, saw that the younger brother had fallen forward on the ground. Immediately the elder brother rushed back, but when he reached the younger brother, the latter was unable to speak, and his eyes were fixed, although his breathing had not yet stopped. Then the elder took him on his lap, untied his own girdle to place him against his own flesh, and put some saliva in the younger brother's mouth, whereupon he revived slightly.

" 'May the six classes of sentient beings not come to experience sufferings such as we two have undergone. May all the sufferings of all sentient beings come upon us two brothers, and at the end of this experience may we become chiefs of faith, drawers of all sentient beings, accomplishing this solely on behalf of sentient beings.' Thus the elder brother, sowing a wish-prayer, wept.

"The younger brother, with staring eyes, said, 'Elder brother, may we two, ourselves in the generations of our rebirths, never part. Today as you, elder brother, went yonder there was a sound from the sky, and my mind was somewhat disturbed. There is also a prophesy from the gods and lamas that there is nothing for me but death. However, you my elder brother, do not become a prey to anguish. May we soon meet.' f 19

After he sowed this wish-prayer, two *Kalaping Ka*[40] birds immediately appeared. 'In the future may we become those who render service to, and are spokesman for, you two brothers.' Such was the wish-prayer they sowed.

"After that, a *Ka Lan Ta Ka* bird[41] alighted. 'May I become one who renders service to you two brothers. Having recalled all the early stories, may I become a learned sage—a compiler of commentaries.'

"Then a cuckoo[42] appeared, 'May I become the majordomo of the pious king *Don aGrub*—the two brothers—and intuitively speak two languages.' Such was his wish-prayer.

"Immediately after this the younger brother's breathing broke off, and the elder brother, holding his ears, cried, 'I the elder brother have thus sent him on.'

"He kissed the cheek of the younger brother and wept profusely. Then without delay, while beside the younger brother's corpse, he sowed this wish-prayer, 'We two were never parted; now I am left

alone. From my father-mother and the kingdom I am like a hair
f 20 pulled from butter. Wandering beyond the borders, I am finally left solitary. Except for the earth and sky there is no one I know. What unrighteousness was accumulated in my former lifetimes to bring such retribution. Oh, that I myself had died and my younger brother were left. However, the phenomenal does not last forever—this is the natural law. If only in the previous existence there had been a lama,[43] a guardian, or a protector, then in this life, without discarding our bodies, we two brothers coming together would have met with our aged father-mother. May I in my mind renounce all unmeritorious and sinful deeds and think that whatever I have of food or possessions are reckoned as gifts to be bestowed willingly. To all mortals certainly comes this, death of the not eternal. It is not far away. Remembering this, when we two brothers ultimately realize the fruits of holiness and the precious doctrine, may we then become the savior-drawers of all sentient beings and as royal representatives may we manifest pure doctrine.'

"Thus sowing measureless wish-prayers, for a short interval he sat in profound contemplation.[44]

"During that interval beasts of prey and birds circumambulated, the earth shook in the six directions; it rained flowers and the gods made music. At that instant a macaque and a langur[45] appeared.
f 21 The two circumambulated him and sowed wish-prayers to become his retainers.

"Then a tiger[46] appeared. 'Of what benefit is a prayer like this from these two to an ordinary person?' he thought as heresy arose in his mind. Mocking the respectful utterance of whatever the other two had said, he spoke in flattery, 'May I too come to be born as a retainer of you two brothers.'

"The prince then broke off perfect contemplation, but still having no thought or assurance of benefit, he carried his younger brother's body on his back. Eight elevations and depressions beyond, halfway up a hill, there was a forest of sandalwood, redwood, juniper, myrobalan, and other such trees. There was also a milk-white waterfall, and under an overhanging cliff he saw a sandalwood tree shaped like a yurt. Coming closer, he saw a rainbow of five colors arched over it. Keeping his eyes fixed on it, he went forward.

In the shadow of the sandalwood tree he made an excellent box of slate slabs[47] to prevent living creatures from disturbing or harming the younger brother, and in it, where fine drops of water were falling, he placed the body.

"His affection was of the utmost. Yet, because of the exigencies of life and because he could not stay in a land of beasts of prey, he went on; weeping and looking back, however, as long as he could see the box of slate slabs that sheltered his brother's body.

"Thence he passed beyond the spurs of thirteen hills.

"Seven days went by, and then an anchorite emanated from Indra of the gods went to that spot carrying a pinch of life-restoring medicine, and a Brahmin emanated from Brahma, carrying a robe of fine cotton cloth, came to the place where the body of Prince *Don Yod* was. f 22

"The body within the box of slate slabs, because of the effect of the fine drops from the sandalwood tree, was not dried out but had remained fresh as though alive.

"The anchorite then put camphor into sandalwood sap and twice spooned it into the mouth of the corpse. After that he sprinkled in life-restoring medicine and spooned some into the mouth, and the body became warm. Again a portion was given, and consciousness returned. When another portion was put into his mouth and one portion was rubbed on his body, he was able to get up and walk.

"The Brahmin presented the robe of fine cotton cloth.

"Then Prince *Don Yod* questioned, 'Who are you two? From what country have you come? You are not my compassionate elder brother; but have you two seen him?'

"The anchorite then said, 'I am empowered by the god to give you life-restoring medicine.'

"After that the Brahmin said, 'Brahma sent me to give you this robe. Your elder brother has gone on beyond eighteen hills and valleys.'

"Again the prince spoke, 'You two have become my benefactors.' Then he made salutations. 'You two thus coming from the god and the realm of men on earth and possessing power such as this, should be able to create the opportunity of a meeting with my elder brother.' f 23

" 'We two will go to look for the elder brother,' they said, and when they had gone about an earshot away, they vanished as a rainbow disappears.

"Prince *Don Yod* then thought, 'This country has only birds, beasts of prey, and game animals.[48] However, my protector-god through these very two—the anchorite and the Brahmin—helped me. Now I will pick some fruit.'

"A macaque that was the emanation of the two presented him with much fruit, but not knowing how to speak or make signs, returned into the forest. He [*Don Yod*] too sought fruit there for food, drank water when thirsty, and wore tree leaves for clothes.

"Each time he ate he would put some choice fruit on a flat stone and cry, 'Eat elder brother; your share of food is here.'

"Then he would weep and cry aloud, 'Elder brother, where are you?'

"He wandered every day among all the hills and in all the forests. Not meeting the elder brother, he suffered and so searched on over all the hills and valleys.

"Just at that time Prince *Don THams Cad aGrub Pa,* having passed beyond the thirteen great hill shoulders, came to a level spot by the path, and while he rested there he noticed that the high f 24 western hill was covered halfway up with forest, and the upper half was a slope of mixed grass and slate scree. Below the grass and scree of the southern face of the slope, at the edge of the forest, he saw clearly the fluttering of light-colored prayer flags and went straight toward the place of the flags.

" 'Although there are neither villagers nor nomads,[49] yet the sight of prayer flags certainly shows that men are here,' he thought.

"So he went steadily forward, and when he arrived at the edge of the forest, halfway up the mountain, he saw human tracks in a line, which he followed, thinking, 'It looks as if there is a hermitage or monastery here.'

"Then he arrived at the edge of the wood where there was a thick clump of trees. From within a fold of the mountain, beyond the prayer flags, he heard the tinkling of small cymbals, and thought, 'Now certainly there is a monastery here,' and became much encouraged.

"Continuing to climb, he came to the head of the fold in the mountain, where there was a spring of water, beside which he saw a somewhat aged monk[50] who wore a monk's robe of fine linen and had set out an oblation beside the spring. The prince made salutations to the lama, and the latter, aroused from profound contemplation, looked up and regarded him as he completed many salutations.

"As a result of his search over many hills and valleys of the Northern Plain, with insufficient food, sorrowing over the death of his younger brother, the prince's hair stood on end; his flesh and skin were dried out and shrunken, and his tattered garments could not cover his private parts. His entire appearance was like one of the hunger demons. Such was the condition in which the lama saw him. f 25

"The lama, by clairvoyance, knew that he was one of the sons of a king and had wandered in exile, but he pretended not to know and said, 'Are you a human being or a hunger demon?'

"The prince: 'With respect, not a hunger demon but the son of a king reduced in circumstances and wandering in exile.' Thus he spoke with respect.

" 'Now where are you going, and where do you stay?' the lama questioned.

"At this the prince made salutation to the lama. 'I have no place to go and no place to stay. From below, seeing the prayer flags, I have come to the lama's residence. Have consideration for me and let me become your servant.' Such was his request.

"Boundless pity for him arose in the lama's mind. 'Then let the two of us go within!'

"This being said, they went on.

"Just beyond there was a great stone the height of two stories. On the east face of the stone the Lord *Od dPag Med* and the Three Lineage Lords[51] were self-manifested, protruding from the stone and about the size of an eight-year-old child. Beside them there was a cave, and over the entrance of the cave there was a shelter of coarse grass. When they arrived there, the lama bathed the prince, shaved his hair, changed his garment to one of good cloth, and gave him wonderful fruit to eat. That was indeed a very pleasant place. f 26

"The lama to the prince: 'Your father, your mother, your birth home—who, what, and where?' So he spoke.

"With no errors or omissions he told his history to the lama.

"The lama was pleased and said, 'After seven days we will examine the auspices. At times the king of this country summons me, but I am aged and somewhat infirm. You, little son, given to me for adoption by the personal deity and the protector of religion, are handsome and possess all the marks.'

"As the servant of the lama he went daily to gather fruit, grass, and firewood, and brought back two bundles of coarse grass. Of one he made a seat mat for the lama and of the other bedding for himself the prince. Every day he swept and cleaned. At sunrise, after seven days had passed, the prince was bathed and, gathering much fruit and food-wood, made innumerable offering-oblations of thanksgiving to the Rare Perfection, the guardian deities, and the protectors of religion. The lama—father-son—the two made effectual wish-prayers. The lama then for a little while passed into the state of profound contemplation, and from thence made an examination of the prince. By great clairvoyance he came to know the future in large part; but he did not tell all. f 27

"Then he said to the prince, 'Prince *Don THams Cad aGrub Pa,* there is no doubt but that you are the emanation of *sPyan Ras gZigs.* It is very wonderful that in this way you patiently endured the former sufferings and did not disobey your father-mother. I perceive good auspices that in the future we—father-son—before we lose these bodies will meet the king—father-mother—and the younger brother. In the interval between, however, there appear to be obstacles for us two—father-son. Supplicate the guardian deities and the protectors of religion and there will be a good and pleasant fulfillment. From this existence, when the time of decadence of Buddha's doctrines comes, we two shall become lords of the doctrine. Gathered with the king—father-mother—and with the younger brother, we all will work for the doctrine and on behalf of sentient beings.' This was his prophesy.

"From that time on, carrying out his duties as servant of the lama, he went out daily to gather fruit and grass.

"A month having passed, the lama said, 'In my mat there never come to be broken, old, or rotted grass stalks, but although you, son, are the emanation of the Lord *sPyan Ras gZigs,* yet your grass is broken and rotted like the grass of ordinary sentient beings. Why is this? You labor much in mind. Without concealing anything from me, tell about it.' f 28

"He answered, 'If I do not tell it to you, the lama, to whom would I tell it? My younger brother, dear as my own heart, is dead; and so when I lie down to sleep at night, sleep does not come. O lama, you are my great benefactor. I wish to have here the bones of my younger brother.' This was his request.

"The lama then said, 'You are of royal descent and without taint; the matchless emanation of the sublime *sPyan Ras gZigs.* Not discarding sublime behavior,[52] you are thus marvelous and of great beauty. By sending you into exile the king—father-mother—have discarded dominion and strength. Tomorrow we—father-son—will go to the place where your younger brother's bones are.'

"The boy *Don THams Cad aGrub Pa* then said, 'You lead the way.'

"The next day the lama—father-son—the two, went in that order for two days and on the third morning arrived at a place in a valley, at the foot of a mountain, where there was a forest and fruit. There they stayed overnight; and birds, beasts of prey, and game animals ranged like a surrounding wall performed circumambulation around the lama—father-son—night and day. The langurs and macaques bringing fruit, their eight lords piled much wonderful fruit in front of the lama—father-son—the two, and performed many salutations and circumambulations.

"The prince then spoke to the lord-father—the lama, 'Birds, beasts of prey, and game animals in great numbers are performing circumambulation; and many langurs and macaques are bringing offerings of homage and bowing down with respect in this manner, which is indeed amazing. Whence such power over them?' f 29

"The lama smiled and said, 'Listen well my son. On behalf of all sentient beings I have come from the breast of the Lord *Od dPag Med,* of Buddha's perfect fields—the heaven of bliss. You, son, have come from Mount Potala in order to be the one who draws sentient beings without number. These sentient beings, understanding the results of such wish-prayers by us—father-son—have now come. In the future, during the period of the doctrine of Gautama northward of *Bhud Gaya,* the cause of many sentient beings will be realized. At that time these birds and animals will be converted to us; many sentient beings of many races and languages will be linked with us; and something of great value will be accomplished.'

"The prince, being astonished, made salutations many times.

"Then, going on, they arrived at the spot where the younger brother's body had been placed. The box of slate slabs was not torn apart, and by it there were fruit peelings and grass used for a bed —traces seemingly of someone who had stayed there. However, none of the younger brother's bones was there. The lama—father-son—stayed there one seven-day period, and daily, on behalf of the younger brother, the lama sowed wish-prayers and performed benedictions and offered oblations. The prince cut grass for the lama's seat mat and collected fruit for offerings. f 30

"As he searched for fruit, the prince mourned and cried in a loud voice, 'Where is my younger brother?' He did not, however, meet him.

"The lama said, 'Your concern for your younger brother is very great and genuine.'

"On the day after five days had passed, the prince went out to collect fruit and search for the younger brother. The lama, having completed oblations, hung up his religious robe in the rays of the sun.

"An injury-bestowing demon said to be a land-owner, having three heads, six arms, and carrying a red spear,[53] arrived at the lama's side.

"He said, 'You lama—father-son—the two of you, do not worry greatly about Prince *Don Yod*. The anchorite gave him life-restoring medicine and, being revived, he has wandered over the hills and valleys seeking his elder brother. For the time being there is no chance for you—father-son—to meet with the younger brother *Don Yod*. Later, however, you will meet with him.'

" 'Who are you?' the lama said.

" 'I am of the race of injury-bestowing demons, and am named *Beg TSi*. In the future when you—father-son—will have become sponsors of the doctrine on behalf of sentient beings without number, I will be your protector.' f 31

"The lama said, 'Very well,' and placed him under oath and gave him orders.

"To the prince, who came back at sundown, the lama said, 'To-day fearsomely there came here one called a land-owner named *Beg TSi*, having three heads, six arms, red in color, and carrying a red spear, who said "You lama—father-son—the two of you—do not worry greatly about Prince *Don Yod*. The anchorite gave him life-restoring medicine and, being revived, he has wandered over the hills and valleys seeking his elder brother. For the time being there is no chance for you—father-son—to meet with the younger brother *Don Yod*. Later, however, you will meet with him."

" 'When questioned, "Who are you?" he answered, "I am of the race of demons, and by name *Beg TSi*. In the future when you—father-son—will have become sponsors of the doctrine on behalf of sentient beings without number, I will act as your protector."

" 'So he promised, and I placed him under oath and under orders and committed the matter to him. The purpose of both of us—father-son—will be fulfilled. Do not be concerned.'

"The prince, delighted, made salutations to the lama. 'Do not forget,' he begged.

"Then, seven days having passed, the lama—father-son—the two, returned. On the path there were nine poisonous snakes,[54] and two lying across it, one behind the other, blocked the way ahead. f 32

"However, the lama thought, 'If I first take a step and touch them there will be no injury.'

"He took a step forward and fell on the two. Then, the son pulling him by the hand, he was able to arise. But the two poisonous snakes had been hurt physically by the pressure.

"The two snakes thought, 'Had not this little boy pulled the lama away, he surely would have killed us.'

"A heretical idea arose in their minds. 'In the future being reborn as personal servants to this little boy, may it come about that we cause dissension between the two of them—father-son.' Such was the rebellious wish-prayer sown. The seven small poisonous snakes, also having similar heretical ideas, fled to a stone slab.

"The lama, however, knowing the heresy and the rebellious wish-prayer of the snakes, and boundless compassion arising, spoke words of truth:

'Many are the generations, obstacles, and heresies.
'The sowers of blasphemous wish-prayers are solely obstructing demons.
'My words have the truth of the sutra.
'Their power will not become the truth.
'The father-son vow, as the knot of the thunderbolt
'Throughout many rebirths, does not become untied.'

"This true saying he uttered.

f 33 "The lama—father-son—then returned to the place of their abode and lived as formerly. Then one day the lama said, 'I remain in seclusion and the meditation of propitiation—that only thus unaffected by pressure and tension. But you, little son, your body is burdened with the daily getting of water, gathering of firewood and fruit, and service to me. That too is pressure and tension. Your mind is oppressed by longing for your younger brother. Being alone, you have no companions with whom to talk. That we may find a way to get rid of tension and the sense of pressure to your body, speech, and mind—all three—let us leave my shelter and go yonder where there is shade and a height from which we can see all the countryside, and there let us stay.'

"Taking wild grain[55] as food and much fruit, they went some distance yonder and stayed as on a holiday. The lama, comfortably seated and at ease, expounded to the boy the doctrine of impermanence.

"Then the prince inquired, 'Lama, with respect, on the great rock yonder at our—father-son—shelter there are reflected likenesses resembling gods. What are those?'

" 'Well-born child, listen carefully. Formerly a Buddha called *Od Mi aGyur* had his abode there. At that time the emanations of f 34 sublime *sPyan Ras gZigs* and *aJam dPal* came as two Brahmin lads to make offerings to that Buddha and he prophesied, 'In the future the two of you gathered together at this place will labor for the cause of the creatures.'[56] It was at that time that these similar figures appeared of their own accord on this cliff. One Buddha shape on this cliff, that of *Ye SHes Od Mi aGyur Ba* is no different from Lord *Od dPag Med.* Of the three who are below it, one is *sPyan Ras gZigs;* at his right is *aJam dByangs;* and at the left is *mTHu CHen THOb Pa;* together being the sons of the Pure Mind *Od dPag Med.*

" 'I am now Lord *Od dPag Med;* you, son, are *sPyan Ras gZigs*; and the younger brother *Don Yod* is *aJam dByangs.* These are the auspices of our being gathered here and of meeting soon with the younger brother—token of the blessing.'[57]

"The prince in joy made salutations; moreover, the gathered birds performed circumambulation. Two winged creatures[58] then

alighted. One presented a bell and the other presented a precious stone.

" 'In the future you—father-son—hold us dear and we will be born as your sponsors.' This perfect wish-prayer they prayed.

"The lama answered, 'Very well,' and promised it.

"Then a partridge[59] appeared with the blasphemous thought f 35 arising:

" 'This lama is like a fake and liar.'

"The lama, being aware of this blasphemy, and compassion arising, said, 'Partridge, do not blaspheme.'

"The partridge nodded his head three times and sowed a wish-prayer to be born the servant of the lama.

"Then the lama—father-son—intoned, without interruption, many prayers for the dead on behalf of the younger brother.

"Once the prince went to a village lower down in the valley to buy wild grain, etc., and on the ground many children were playing. Seeing his marvelous appearance, all were amazed.

" 'Where do you come from?' they questioned.

" 'Just a beggar's child,' he answered and said no more.

"He then played with them, and when he was leaving they pounded grain and gave it to him.

"That day when he returned, he told the lama about the matter.

"The lama said, 'Son, you did well today. Do not give detailed explanations, for if you do there is a risk that the king might take you away by force.'

"Every other day he did this to get grain, and when the children gathered he became the leader. He contended with those of the same age and won over all of them.

"At that, the prince then boasted, 'I am of the Dragon Year and so the sound of my fame is greater than the sound of the dragon.[60] I am also above all.'

"In that country on the plain beyond, five leagues from the hermitage, there was the sky-high castle of a king surrounded by one hundred thousand dwellings. Around all this there was a great wall with a hundred turrets and a thousand gates. Within there f 36 was a king called *Gocha,* the emanation of *PHyag rDor,*[61] who had no children with the exception of a daughter—as amazingly beautiful as light.

"At a distance of two leagues from the palace there was a great sea about six leagues in circumference. There, on the fifteenth of the first moon of summer, a turquoise blue dragon used to come down from the sky and, with dragon sound, enter the sea. When this happened, the king, ministers, and subjects made offerings, and through their efficacy timely rain came and the course of continuing sickness to men and beasts was cut off.

"This propitious time had however ended. The live dragon no longer came down into the sea; it no longer rained; men and beasts fell sick; and there was famine.

"The king ordered divination.

"The female diviner[62] said, 'In this sea are the kings of the Nagas:[63] *dGaa Bo* and *NYer dGaa*; and others such as *Bha Su Ra, Wa Ru Na, Lag Mangs, Na Ga De Ba, EH La aDab Ma.* There is now no other method. A three-times-six-year-old of the Fire Dragon Year, carrying what the Nagas require and token articles—the wheel and written spells—bound to him, must be thrown into the sea. Then it will become as before.' Thus the prophesy.

"The king did as directed, and it rained as before. This was done every year and those Dragon-Year ones who were seventeen- or eighteen-years-old fled if they could. f 37

"In any case, whenever the kings and his ministers, ceremonially wearing finest ornaments and making offerings and sowing prayers to the sea, threw a Fire-Dragon-Year one into that sea, their hopes, in heaped-up measure, were realized.

"The time for throwing a man into the sea having come, the king sent his ministers to look for the required youth, a Dragon-Year one who was eighteen-years-old. They were not able, however, to find one.

"King *Gocha's* fated[64] minister named *Trishu* was present: one who was envious and burning with anger, insane with the three poisons, doubting the word of Buddha, and always delighted to carry a cutting weapon of any sort. He was the one responsible for throwing many persons alive into the sea. Because of his zeal in this, his frustrated purpose, he heard from those other children the rumor that Prince *Don THams Cad aGrub Pa* was a Dragon-Year one just eighteen years of age and living with Lama *Legs Pa Blo Gros* as a disciple. With satisfaction he reported back to the king.

" 'Bring him immediately!' was the order.

"The minister Trishu started for the lama's shelter.

"Before the messenger-minister arrived, however, the lama by f 38 clairvoyance was aware of it, and said, 'Well-born son, the king's fearsome one comes to the two of us to take you away by force. Son, now hide yourself in the grass.'

He then hid in the far end of the interior of the shelter, where there was much coarse grass, and an earthenware pot was placed upside down over the grass.

"The lama said, 'Until I say so do not appear. If they hear your voice, they will take you and throw you into the sea.'

"The minister then arrived, and the lama quickly came to the entrance of the shelter.

"*Trishu* then said, 'Lama, there is a boy here with you. The king sends me to bring him. Tell me where he is.'

" 'I have no one to aid me in the effort of realization. I am a monk practicing the meditation of realization. How could there be a boy to a solitary man?' Thus he spoke.

" 'If you do not tell, it will not be well with the lama's own self.'

" 'On my part there is nothing to say. I am a man alone, devoted to the effort of realization. I have no one I desire or love. If you want to kill me, then go ahead and kill me.' He said this in a take-it-or-leave-it manner.[65]

"Pushing into the shelter and searching, but finding nothing, the minister *Trishu* then said, "Kill the lama!" and threatened him with the sword.[66]

"The prince, seeing this from under the grass, thought, 'This, my benefactor lama will be killed if I do not go. This is not right.'

"The prince then showing himself from out of the grass said, f 39 'Do not treat my benefactor lama like this.'

" 'This is the child,' he said, and took him away, holding him by the hand.

"The lama was not able to seize him.

"Blasphemy welling up within him, the minister *Trishu* said to the lama, 'You, fake monk, if you have no wife, and the child's father and mother are of some unknown land and origin, how is it possible for you to have a child like this?'

"Thinking this, and showing it in speech, he struck him three blows on the chest, and, as the lama fell backwards, they got away.

"Early and late, without ceasing, the lama made wish-prayers and, sowing supplications to the Rare Perfection, composed the following:

'Lamas, guardians, protectors of religion all,
'On me turn your thoughts and in compassion save.
'This perfect son is the compassionate emanation of the Rare Perfection;
'Given by the god and lama in bounteous fulfillment.
'Take away the hindrance by the devil's emanation.
'Do not let my son experience suffering.
'We, father-son, are of many births.
'Now the wish-prayer of soon meeting is sown.'

"These true aphorisms he uttered.

"So they arrived before King *Gocha*.

"The king, pleased, remarked, 'The little boy is handsome.'

"For seven days he stayed in the palace, and the daughter of the king, the goddess one *Od lDan Ma,* beautiful and full of light, lost her heart[67] to the prince; it seemed as though the prince and she, being happy and in harmony, could not bear to be apart. f 40

"The set time of the sea[68] drew near, but the king said, 'This my daughter and this little boy cannot bear to be apart. You ministers, go and find another Dragon-Year eighteen-year-old one.'

"The other ministers were not able to say anything, but the minister *Trishu* said, 'The king speaks once only; but if many times—in this fashion the law of the realm will break down, the people will revile the king.'

"This he said in a take-it-or-leave-it manner.

"Then he added, 'This is not a lama in good standing. Without a wife how can he have a child like this? The lama is not a devotee but a fake.'

"Then into the mind of the prince came these thoughts, 'If I am not able to abandon this goddess one *Od lDan Ma,* some other man, being found, will have to go for me. What a pity!'

"Thus from a loving mind which held others more dear than himself, the prince made a suggestion to the ministers. 'This daughter, the goddess one, holding me thus, we cannot come apart. Let some of you athlete-ministers and the two of us all go together in a boat for getting gems. When the daughter is asleep, you your-

selves seize the goddess one and do not let her go. I, on behalf of the six classes of sentient beings, without any hesitation will then pass into the sea.'

"When he had so spoken the ministers and people all were struck with astonishment and marveled. f 41

"At that time the ministers *Zla Bas Byin* and *Ka rTi Ka,* the two arising, made salutations and wept. 'At the end remember also us two!' they requested.

"The prince, the goddess one, the athlete-ministers, the retainers, and so forth, then got into the boat and departed. But day and night the daughter, the goddess one, would not let go, but held on to the prince. Finally, after an interval, the hand of the daughter loosened, and, signaling with his hand to the ministers, the prince jumped into the great sea.

"From the sky came sound, light, a rainbow, and a rain of flowers. The earth moved, and in the intermediate space there was thunder—a dragon—lightning, and so forth.

"Holding on to the daughter, the ministers returned to the palace.

"The king and the two ministers together repented and made confession for what had been done. And as for the daughter, the goddess one, she too was overwhelmed with sorrow.

"At that time in the center of the great ocean the Naga king *NYer dGaa* and such chiefs as *aDZin Pa Lag Mangs,* together with male and female Nagas in inconceivable numbers, were at the palace of *NYer dGaa.* Then the prince, covered as with drops of dew, arrived among them. They arose before the handsome prince and greeted him with all courtesy and reverence.

"After which they said, 'Formerly a person—body and mind ripped apart—was sacrificed with great lamentations; and bloody rain fell on the country of the Nagas. Now with your coming, pious king, there is the sound of music. Flowers, fruits, nutmeg, and excellent Naga medicines fall with the rain. Our region becomes productive. Because of this force, sentient beings foresake malice; the Nagas have long life and prosper, and even when they die they are reborn as gods and in human form. There is great joy.' f 42

"At that point the Nagas said to the prince, 'Are you going upward to your own country? Remain and be the lord of us, who are the Naga creatures.'

"The prince said, 'Since I exist on behalf of sentient beings, where I am makes no difference. However, my lama, who is the peerless emanation of the Lord *Od dPag Med,* is prey to anxiety. At some time I wish to go. Do not be envious or begrudge me this, but give me leave.'

"He told them in order all the previous history. The Naga kings, beginning with *dGaa Bo EH La* and *NYer dGaa Bo,* and six million assembled Nagas lauded him and made many and great salutations and offerings.

"For three months, counting as men count,[69] he stayed in Naga-land and preached the doctrine.

f 43

"The Nagas then respectfully said, 'Through your compassion those of us, gods and Nagas, whose bodies and sense organs had deteriorated have been healed. Wealth has increased and well-being exists in triple perfection. Because of your compassion, in the future it will not be necessary for men to be thrown alive into this sea.'

"Then the two Naga kings, *NYer dGaa* and *EH La,* each presented a gem of wish fulfillment the size of a goose egg as the principal gift among valuable jewels. The Nagas *Dung sKyongs* and *aDZin Ba Lag Mangs* also presented many gems of different kinds of lapis lazuli, and the Naga subjects also presented different gems. All sowed wish-prayers. The prince promised to keep them always in mind. The Nagas in this manner bade him farewell.

"The prince, however, closing his eyes, sowed the wish-prayer, 'May I come to my lama's side.'

"Instantly he came to the entrance of the lama's shelter.

"He said, 'Oh, that my lama should be in this condition! But now that I have arrived, have no worry.'

" 'My son in this manner was thrown into the sea. There is no chance of his returning from the dead. Do you say this to comfort my heart or to disturb my mind?' Saying this, he fainted.

"The lama, being sprinkled with sandalwood water from a jar, revived. Having eaten stew made of dried meat and being rubbed with the grease,[70] he was glad. His eyes being cleansed of accumulated mucous, the prince embraced him around the neck.

f 44

"He said, 'I am *Don aGrub.*'

"The lama was glad that in this manner the dead and the living came to meet and questioned the prince about what had happened.

The prince then told in detail his own history. And also all that he had brought in the folds of his garment, beginning with the gem of wish fulfillment, he gave to the lama.

" 'Rare in the world is one like this my son—emanation's king. He is benefactor to the six classes of sentient beings.'

"The two—father-son—when sitting, sat on the same mat; when eating, ate from the same dish; and could not bear to be separated.

"At that time King *Gocha* said, 'Since our lama's son, the young boy, was thrown into the sea, the harvest is more bountiful than before, sickness has disappeared, rain falls at the right time, and perfect accumulated contentment and happiness abound. We should invite the lama here, and extend hospitality to him.'

"All the ministers agreed.

"But the minister *Trishu* did not like it and said, 'The lama is one of our own. For a ruler to show gratitude and so honor a subject is not proper.'

"The other ministers, however, voiced agreement.

"The king then commanded, 'Whoever among the ministers has faith in and honors the lama, let him go to extend the invitation.'

"Then the minister called *CHos dPal aBar* said, 'I shall go,' and, taking a group of ten retainers, he left. f 45

"Arriving before the lama, he said, 'O lama, the Great Value One,[71] with respect, because your son, Prince *Don THams Cad aGrub Pa,* was thrown in the lake, all our realm is perfectly content and happy. In gratitude for this, in order to honor the lama, the king offers peerless gifts and I am sent to extend an invitation. Let us go.'

" 'This being the case, rest over there a little and when I have changed into my religious robe, I will come.' he said. He was thinking, however, 'To go and leave the boy behind is not to be thought of. Yet to take him along involves the risk that when the king sees him, he may want to take him by force.'

"The prince suggested, 'Disguised as a beggar and wearing a cloth mask over my face, it will be all right for me to go as a servant.'

" 'Well then, let us make a mask so that it will be all right to go.' Saying this, he disguised the prince with a cloth mask as a beggar and servant. The prince carrying the lama's cloak and ritual objects, they set out.

"Then the minister said to the lama, 'Please mount your horse."

" 'No, I have given up all riding,' the lama said, and holding the prince by the hand, the two went on foot.

"The minister then questioned the lama, 'From what country is this your attendant, and why cannot he show his face?'

"The lama answered, 'This my attendant was given to me by a poor beggar. He cannot show his face because, as this beggar child came a long way over the Northern Plain, on the way his face received injury from poisonous flies and is broken out in sores. Until f 46 his face heals he cannot show it; the sun and wind must not strike it.'

"Thus they arrived at the palace of King *Gocha*. The lama was placed on a seat made up of three cushions and the attendant, the prince, was placed on a small rug which had been spread. The lama—father-son—each presented fruit as hand-gifts.

"The king then said to the lama, 'I wish you to remain here a week.' To this the lama agreed.

"Perfect hospitality was extended with reverence, and the king said to the lama. 'Be patient with me because I had to do this and send the only son of the holy lama into the sea and cause the lama sorrow. After the son passed into the sea, perfect contentment and happiness came to all sentient beings. It is because of our gratitude for this that you were invited here.'

"The lama answered, 'Very well. King, ministers, all of you together, listen.'

"He then recounted the tale of the prince, and all were amazed and made salutations to the lama.

"Four days passed and no one recognized the prince. On the day following the fifth night, while the lama and the king were walking on the roof of the palace with the ministers, the daughter, that goddess one *Od lDan Ma,* having in her hands a rhinoceros horn together with an elephant tusk and the skin of the black antef 47 lope, offered them to the lama and, making salutations, sought a blessing.

" 'Prince *Don THams Cad aGrub Pa* is gone into the sea. Bear this in mind,' she begged and wept.

"The lama was moved with boundless tenderness. 'By the grace of the god-lama there is no harm. The prince and yourself, you two, fated by your former destiny, will meet.'

"Just as he was speaking a great whirlwind came up and blew off the lama's hat. The prince bent down hastily to catch it, and his head bumped into an elephant's nose[72] of the parapet. As he bumped his head, the tie strings of the mask were broken and his face could be seen.

"Then the ministers spoke up, 'O prince welcome,' and made salutations.

"The king-father and the daughter, the goddess one, both recognized the prince. The daughter seized the prince, and they embraced each other, saying, 'That the dead and living should meet in this way!'

"King *Gocha,* the ministers, and the people, all together, were greatly astonished. All presented splendid gifts beginning with gems each of a different kind.

" 'How did this come about?' they questioned the lama.

"How the lineage son of King *Bhala Deva* was exiled and how he went to the country of the Nagas was told in detail, and they were all amazed.

"Then the prince, and the goddess one too, went to the lama's shelter to get the gems of the Nagas. f 48

"The lama then gave to the king the gem of wish fulfillment and to each minister a different kind of gem.

"The king then made a confession: 'I did not know that you were a great prince. Because the person of the son was maltreated, the lama's mind was disturbed. Thus there is the guilt of the sin and fault of body, speech and mind—all three. Be patient. In the lifetimes of my rebirths, please remember me.'

"On a high golden throne topped with three layers of cushions the lama, the Great Value One, took his seat. On a high silver throne topped with two layers of cushions Prince *Don THams Cad aGrub Pa* took his seat. Then on a turquoise throne topped with one cushion the daughter, the goddess one *Od lDan,* took her seat, and the king himself took a seat on two cushions. In this manner threefold and perfect courtesy and reverence were shown.

"The King *Gocha* suggested to the lama: 'This king *Don THams Cad aGrub Pa* indeed is able to maintain a kingly line. The manner of his deeds suggests magical transformations; and to seek and find such a one in the world is not possible. This girl cannot be separated from this prince, who is fated by wish-prayers.[73]

f 49 I have no son in my line of descent. No other one is suitable as a successor. What is in the lama's holy mind?'

" 'Meritorious king, you and we—father-son—are the fruit of wish-prayers. This my son is the emanation of the sublime *sPyan Ras gZigs.* Remember that with respect,' the lama answered.

" 'O lama, will you consult the planets, stars, and so forth?' he asked.

" 'Counting upward after thirteen nights, that day is good!' he answered.

"The king said, 'When this king *Don THams Cad aGrub Pa* has been raised to *Gocha's* place, then I also will take the monastic vow. The lama and myself, the two of us, will build a monastery within the country in a pleasant place among the mountains where there is grass, water, and trees. There I will stay.'

"Then subordinates, leaders, officials, vassal kings, and such were assembled, and it was proclaimed to them and throughout the land: 'King *Don THams Cad aGrub Pa* is about to assume rule over the king's realm. After thirteen days and nights have passed, on the following day pay homage and offer gifts to him.'

"On the day when the planets and the stars were well met, the king, the lama, and the daughter, the goddess one, together sat on their respective thrones. King *Gocha* then presented to the two, the king and the daughter, as the principal gifts many ordinary and extraordinary gems of wish fulfillment and marvelous ritual objects symbolic of Buddha's word; also gifts of gold, lapis lazuli, f 50 volumes of the Scriptures, much fine silk, cloth, quantities of real gold and silver coins—all loaded on many elephants. In addition to that, there were horses, buffaloes, and such in great number.

"King *Don THams Cad aGrub Pa* and the daughter, the goddess one *Od lDan,* becoming father-mother,[74] were appointed to the place of the king. Flags were raised, trumpets were blown, music was made, and singing, dancing, and similar activities went on for many days and nights.

"At that time the hundred ministers proffered hospitality, each one for a day, for a hundred days.

"But as for the minister *Trishu,* he still had not developed faith; he thought, 'This impostor monk is like a tricky magician, yet in his talk he pretends to have marvelous faith and devotion and that he acts accordingly.'

"The following day, the minister *Trishu* invited the lama—the Great Value One—the king and the prince, etc., all of them together, and throughout three days and nights entertained them with perfect hospitality.

"The prince preached the doctrine, but still faith did not arise in his mind.

"Yet, hypocritically, he begged, 'May I be reborn among your attendants?'

"But the prince granted his request, saying, 'In the future you will be a lord among those around me.'

"King *Gocha* then took the monastic vows from the lama; and three hundred of his subjects became monks.

"In that region a magnificent monastery was established. The lama was asked to name it, and he gave it the name of *Sukar*. The lama tied them with the rules of religion as with a tight knot. He ordained King *Gocha* and three hundred of his official-servants as monks, and called the king by the religious name of *dGe Ba dPal*. To each one of the others he also gave a religious name. f 51

"Then the lama, the monks, and attendants all together left for the monastery.

"The king—father-mother—protected the kingdom, so that it spread and prospered. Two years having passed, King *Don THams Cad aGrub Pa* thought, 'My kingdom expands in accordance with religion. I have met the lama, and perfect contentment and happiness exist, but if my younger brother is dead, I must search for his bones. If he is alive, I must see where he is. Until now I have disregarded the lama's encouraging prophesy. As elder brother, my mind having become corrupt, I have abandoned him. Why has this been?' Such thoughts arising, his sadness grew.

"The numerous ministers being assembled, he gave the order, 'Prepare horses and elephants and provisions for a month. Official-servants all, in this time when everything expands and is prosperous, let us go for my consolation to the Northern Plain, the forests, and such places.'

"He himself then went out, following his old course. In the empty region he built villages for habitation; he dug up and ploughed fallow land into fields; and where there was no water he drew out water. Upon his poor subjects he bestowed the bounty of food, wealth, and fields. f 52

"Then King *Don THams Cad aGrub Pa* and his retinue arrived at the place where Prince *Don Yod* had died; and the ministers reported, 'There is something in this area which was not here before. It is the figure of a man, with hair grown on the body as on the body of a monkey, whose cries resound over there in the hollow.'

"When the ministers made this report, the king, still longing for the younger brother, mourned and said, 'You yourselves, together with the people and attendants, stay wherever it is pleasant and amuse yourselves. I and a few of my attendants will go to that hollow over there to bathe and walk around.'

"Taking with him certain ones as servants he went on.

"As he went, he thought, 'It seems that I may meet the younger brother today,' and great gladness arose.

"Then he said, 'Let us go where this living creature is said to be,' and went on.

"Beyond the hollow there was a forest, and from deep within the forest there came a resounding outcry.

" 'The rest of you stay here,' he said and, crouching, he crept slowly forward.

"A fearsome one, human body overgrown with fur, carried fruit and the flesh of animals and, making great outcry, kept saying, 'Where does elder brother *Don aGrub* stay?'

f 53 "At that King *Don aGrub* wept, 'From among the dead he thus looks for me. As for me, can it be I have neglected what I should do?'

"Thinking this, he said, *'Don Yod, Don Yod,* I am here.'

"As he said this, the younger brother listened with his ears cocked, and then the king—saying, 'Elder brother is here'—approached him.

"The younger brother then thinking, 'It is my elder brother's voice,' set out running and the brothers clasped hands.

"The prince said, 'My younger brother comes in this manner.'

"The younger brother with joyful voice, 'Myself, I meet the elder brother.'

"The two then wept for joy.

"The younger brother's hair was sheared with an eating knife, and the two brothers went to where the others were.

"When the princes—the two brothers—met each other, grief

disappeared. From this comes the story called the disappearance of grief.

"The excess body hair of the younger brother was shaved off with a razor. Five kinds of nectar were placed in his mouth, and his body became like that of his brother.

"At the place where the prince died, water sprang out and flowed from the left and right, making a pool. A monastery was built and a continuous flow of merit was created.

"As the brothers went along the way, they planned the establishment of villages, and then sent swift messengers ahead to the palace. When the story of how the younger had died and been restored to life was told, the courtiers were all struck with astonishment. The two brothers and the attendants then returned together to the palace.

f 54

"The daughter, the goddess one *Od lDan* at the head of many women and men; the pious ministers *Dzaya Dhara* and *Anandha; Trishu,* the fated minister preceding them; and many men, adorned with their best ornaments—all came out to welcome them. At the palace flags were flown, there was matchless music, and dancing, masquerades, and amusements; a sky-high celebration took place. The lama and King *dGe Ba dPal* were also invited. All were amazed, and faith arose in them.

"At that time, however, the minister *Trishu* thought, 'This impostor monk, using the method of magical illusions, caused his own son to get the place of the king. As if this were not enough, he took occasion to bring this younger brother, who was wandering in the border regions, and will bring the brothers together. As for the present, although I am quite capable, and somewhat better than most of the ministers, he—father-urchin[75]—holding against me what was done before, will not treat me well.' With such thoughts his suspicions grew.

"King *Don THams Cad aGrub Pa*—the brothers two—then each sat on a golden throne. The lama congratulated and consecrated them. Rejoicing and festivities went on for seven years.

"Then the minister *Trishu* had evil thoughts and made friends with the robber chief of the district of *bZung THag* of the country of *Gang Ga,* who came to attack.

"Prince *Don Yod,* as commander of the troops, defeated them.

"When the minister was brought before the two brothers, he

begged for pardon, and they increased his former status and responsibility threefold until he was satisfied. Nevertheless, the mind of faith did not develop in him. f 55

"All the subjects of the realm being content, kings from beyond the border came to render homage.

"Then into the mind of King *Don THams Cad aGrub Pa* came these thoughts: 'The service to the lama has been accomplished. Also I have rejoined the younger brother, who from death is restored to life. The wish-prayers sown have been effective. As for me, I now go to meet the two—the father-mother.'

"He then consulted with the younger brother and the lady, and they said, 'Very well.'

"The pious minister *dPal aBar* and the minister *Trishu* were installed in King *Gocha's* palace. Then taking a gem of wish fulfillment[76] as the principal gift, the seven items of great value,[77] articles of gold and silver, and numerous products of the realm to the amount of many elephant loads, father-mother—the three—set out. They were attended by the pious minister *Dzaya Dhara,* by *Anandha,* and in addition followed by a thousand ministers.

"When the king's builders of new villages were working near the country of the father-mother, the rumor was, 'It seems that a very great powerful foreign king comes to seize our country by force.'

"Hearing this report, the father-mother were in great fear. This was in addition to the worry they already felt, not being able to rid themselves of their sorrow over the absence of the two brothers.

"The prince brothers sent one hundred messengers as advance guards to the palace of the father-mother, but all the people spread a great rumor that war was coming. Then the pious minister *Dzaya Dhara,* with retainers, making a total of five, went to the palace. f 56

" 'The brother princes *Don THams Cad aGrub Pa* and *Don Yod,* and the lady, through us, inform you that they are coming to meet with the father-mother,' he announced.

" 'How can this be possible? King *Gocha* comes to take my place by force,' said the king.

"The ministers and people were in fear and said, 'What can we do?'

"The messenger then set up a camp on the plain, near the palace of the father-mother and stayed there one night.

"The two princes again sent messengers—five official-servants—

to the place of the father-mother, and within a dispatch box a letter that told the story of the difficulties the brothers encountered when they were in exile.

"After that, five official-retainers were dispatched with an official letter that told of the circumstances of the younger brother *Don Yod's* death and of the meeting with the lama.

"Finally, messengers carried a letter that told of the manner in which the younger brother was restored to life and reunion, of the manner of the elder brother's going into the country of the Nagas, and of how the realm of King *Gocha* was taken over. Thus, first and last, messengers were sent three times.

"The father-mother, the ministers, and the people were all struck with amazement, and marvelled. There was no limit to their rejoicing. Immediately flags were unfurled against the sky, and the land was filled with songs, music, sports, loud rejoicing, and so forth.

f 57 "The king-father, *Bhala Deva,* had not previously put a foot outside the great gate of the palace. Now, taking a turquoise staff in his hand, he said, 'I am going to meet my two sons and the bride.'

"Many ministers assembled and went out to welcome them. The prince brothers, together with the lady, halted at the entrance of the tent and, offering hand-gifts, met the father-mother. With great joy they embraced one another and stayed in the camp for three days, and the place was adorned with the eight emblems of good fortune.[78]

"Then the mother, the goddess one *Padma,* brought the gem of wish fulfillment and many varieties of gems such as white gems, lapis lazuli, gems of the three colors—yellow, green, and white—emeralds, blue sapphires, ornaments of the seven different gems, along with a wealth of horses, elephants, silk, and cloth; presents without number were offered with salutations.

"The king then said to pious King *Don THams Cad aGrub Pa,* 'I did not realize who you were in your magical transformations. Forgive my pride, cruelty, and evil intentions. You the two brothers have in your hands the comfort or suffering of your two aged parents.' With many tears, making many salutations, they prostrated themselves at the feet of the princes.[79]

"Then King *Don THams Cad aGrub Pa* answered:

'I know the six classes as father and mother.
'Whence either resentment or affection?
'Completely separated from envy or discrimination, f 58
'What is either nearness or farness?
'That done by the mother became friendship's act.'

"When he spoke these words, the father-mother, all the ministers, and all the subjects were able to attain the faith of the believing mind.

"The ministers and the subjects, together with the attendants, then went to the *bKra SHis brTSegs* (Heaped-up Good Fortune) palace.

"King *Don Yod* was appointed to take the father-king's place, there being in general no difference between the realms of the two brothers. The one lady also was adequate.[80] As the people became increasingly prosperous and expanded, the two ruled over two thirds of the entire world.

"The minister *Trishu* being appointed the commander of the troops, the vassal kings of the four borders by the power of faith were gathered as subjects.

"Then on one occasion King *Don THams Cad aGrub Pa* said, 'I wish to send an envoy to invite my benefactor and King *dGe Ba dPal aBar.*' So he sent one.

"The lama, the Great Value One, and King *dGe Ba dPal,* accompanied by 30,000 members of the monastic community, came to the palace.

"When they had arrived at *bKra SHis brTSegs* palace, Lama *Legs Pa Blo Gros* took his seat on a great high golden throne at the highest level.[81] At the right, a silver throne was set up and King *dGe Ba dPal,* the father-king *Bhala Deva* and the mother *Padma Can* all sat there. At the left, a golden throne was set up; King *Don THams Cad aGrub Pa* sat there. King *Don Yod* sat on a silver throne lined-up with it, and the lady *Od lDan Ma* took her seat on a turquoise throne in line. f 59

"Then *Grom Pa Blo Gros Ye SHes Tog, rGyal mTSHan dPal, NYe Mas sByin,* and others of the community of monks and attendants, to the number of many tens of thousands; Karna, the female diviner, *Bhadra,* the discerner of signs, and others; many

Brahmins, the pious minister *CHos dPal aBar,* and *Dzaya Dhara, Anandha, Zla Bas Byin, Ka rTi Ka,* and so forth; and the ministers of the court, in all many tens of thousands, were assembled there in one place and celebrated with inconceivable joy.

"Throughout three months and a score of days and nights, the lama then preached the doctrine, principally setting forth in its order the law of causality,[82] and then he told the story of the many amazing deeds of Prince *Don THams Cad aGrub Pa.*

"At that time he prophesied:

" 'In the future time of decadence, we ourselves will be in that land about two hundred leagues northward from here, which is filled with goblins, carnivorous demons, and beasts of prey, where the sound of the holy religion does not exist—the barbarian frontier called the region of the snow mountains. At the time the "once gone one" called Gautama comes into the world, where now it is like an ocean, the doctrine of the "once gone one" will spread over the barbarian border region then filled with human beings, and the holy religion will spread and increase.

f 60

" 'There you, Prince *Don THams Cad aGrub Pa,* will civilize the land. In that land, you first as king, called by the name of *bTSan,*[83] will have perhaps from three to seven rebirths and will begin to establish the practice of the holy religion.'

" 'In those times, younger brother *Don Yod,* you will most often appear as the son. As for me, once or twice I will be father; but generally I will be the lama who makes offerings. Maintaining the behavior and customs of a monk, I will serve the interest of many creatures.'

" 'Also at the time of the slight decline of the doctrine, in the sublime land, I will appear as a CHANG CHUB SEMPA, *Dibam Gara* by name, and will be an abbot[84] in Tibet. Son *Don THams Cad aGrub Pa,* becoming the one named *Dzaya,*[85] will be the most able of my disciples. Younger brother *Don Yod,* [86] you, in becoming the one named *Pradzanya* who belongs to me, should be unrivaled in doctrinal achievement on behalf of all creatures. In the end time of disputations and decadence we two—abbot-pupil—father-son—will not be apart. Younger brother, you as sponsor, in the royal manner will benefit the creatures.'

" 'Some born as universal monarchs and sponsors, as chiefs of the monk assemblies, will draw many of the creatures. Some will

f 61

be in the father-mother manner.[87] In the era of those who are fortunate and blessed you will gather them here. Some as abbot vice-regents of Buddha or as disciples, acting as leaders of the monastic community, will draw many creatures. Some maintaining the father-mother manner will be able to exercise wish-prayer power. Some born as universal monarchs will behave as sponsors. Some having faith and scholarship will become our disciples. Some, even though of mean birth, seeing our face—father-son—and hearing our words, will be able to have faith and seize upon the stage of the CHANG CHUB SEMPA.'

"Thus he uttered prophesies.

"All who were assembled were amazed, believed, and made salutations to the lama—father-sons—the three. And according to what each felt was fitting, they presented offerings and hand-gifts.

"As for the minister *Trishu,* because he still had not given up heresy, he thought, 'I will act without letting *CHos dPal aBar,* the minister who is staying in the palace of King *Gocha,* know.' So he took a hundred robbers with him, thinking, 'That charlatan magician lama by his own might has caused these two boys to gain both realms. About this lama—father-sons—since I am unable to maltreat and master them, I will flee beyond the border.'

"Then as he went along a narrow place in the path, a landslide ended the span of his life.

"From that time on, the king and subjects prospered expansively and the districts supporting the monastic community were greatly increased in number. Throughout many reigns contentment was created like that in the land of the gods.

"The telling of the secret biography of King *sPyan Ras gZigs Don THams Cad aGrub Pa,* as I know it, is ended. f 62

"Except to the blessed ones and those of faith, he who reveals this history to anyone else is on the path of heresy, and is in danger of falling into hell.[88] The end.

"King *Don THams Cad aGrub Pa* of that time and period is now His Honor the Perfect Victorious Power himself.[89] As to the excellent Lama *Blo Gros* of that time, I am he.[90] King *Gocha* of that time is the former prime minister.[91] The minister *Trishu* of that time is now this prime minister himself.[92] The mother of King *Don aGrub* of that time now is the mother.[93] Of the nine blasphemous snakes by the road, of that time, one or more are also now with us, and of the others, several are among the members of the peak and base:[94] still they do us no harm." Thus he spoke.

Again salutations were made.

"Are there any others of that time now present?" we asked.

There being no clear answer as to whether there are any now present, the question was asked again.[95]

"Of the others of that time I think that the younger brother *Don Yod* is now the prime minister *AH Bar,* the son of the medial one of high position. As for the two *Kalaping Ka* birds, I think they are respectively the emanation-body of *De Mo*[96] and this the great wizard.[97] As for the female diviner *Karna,* she, I think, is *Blo bZang Byams Pa* his very self. As for the *Ka Lan Ta Ka* bird, he is the *rJe Drung Blo bZang Nor Bu.*[98] The cuckoo of that time who sowed the wish-prayer is now *Dar rGyas CHos sDings Pa,*[99] the revealer of hidden treasures. As for the minister *dPal aBar,* he is *PHun TSHogs Rab brTan,*[100] the treasurer. As for the pious minister *Dzaya Dhara,* he is *sByin Pa,* the manager of *rNam rGyal* college.[101] As for the discerner of signs, *Bhadra,* he is *CHos rGya mTSHo,* the chant leader. That pious minister *Rab brTan* is now the valet. *Zla Bas Byin* is *rTag Tu gNas* the *bKaa Blon*[102] of the central authority. Concerning the langur and macaque who sowed wish-prayers, that langur is King *Dha Lag Ba Dur* and that macaque is the chamberlain *mNGaa Rigs* the *ZHal SNa Nas*[103]. The father-king *Bhala Deva himself* is *bsTan aDZin CHos rGyal.*[104] As for the pious *Ka rTi Ka,* he is now *rGyal Po KHri Ba.*[105] The mother *Padma Can is the ZHabs Drung* of *gYon Ru.*[106] As for that daughter of King *Gocha,* she is *Gling Yag Pa*[107] the abbot of *dGe lDan* monastery. As for the partridge who sowed the blasphemous wish-prayer, he now is that retainer who, in the guise of a monk, creates dissension between me and the High All-Knowing One. As for the two winged creatures, they are, respectively, the Chinese *Bog rDo* and the king of those *Hor.*[108] The birds and wild animals which performed circumambulation have become sponsor kings. Those who had faith in us—father-son—are the many vassal kings of the north.

f 63

f 64

"Also among our servants are the pious ones and such saints as *Blo Gros,* and so forth to the number of a hundred, *CHab mDo aPHags Pa La,*[109] and many great lamas of our side who are living.

In many previous births they had the power to project faith and devotion and achieve rebirth.

"We have told this to you here conversationally, like the epic of King Gesar, and as a dream is projected.

"The minister *Trishu* in rebirth is this very same prime minister who had not an instant of faith in us. Nevertheless, no harm develops. The end." Thus his utterance.

All those gathered then performed salutations and voiced agreement.

Like this it is noted on paper. Do not tell it to all. In general the prime minister is severe. If he hears and is angry it will be disastrous. In particular if that which is beyond the comprehension of common people is shown to those who are unblessed, it becomes the cause for condemnation. Also the one himself who reveals it occasions sin and is in danger of being overwhelmed by the guardians. Only between those who have faith: from others keep it secret.

This is made for those who have faith in the holy one who leads the creatures. Also by this record, in every direction and at all times, may Buddha's doctrine spread and increase. f 65

The great cause of the rescue of the creatures being fulfilled, the merit from carving the woodblocks of this story extends without discrimination to all creatures; they shall partake of the happiness of the perfect age. At the end may they attain the stage of the Buddhahood. *Sarba mangalom!*[110] Let good fortune come![111]

The Tibetan script on the following pages was copied from the edited woodblock text by the Reverend Cho-gyatso.

༄༅། །དཔལ་ལྡན་བླ་མ་དམ་པ་
རྗེ་བཙུན་བློ་བཟང་ཡེ་ཤེས་ཀྱི་གསུང་
ལས་གསང་བའི་རྣམ་ཐར་བཞུགས་སོ། །

༄༅། །ཤིང་ཕོ་སྟག་གི་ལོ་ས་ག་ཟླ་བའི་དུས་ཆེན་ཉིན།

དཔལ་ལྡན་བླ་མ་དམ་པ་ཁྱབ་བདག་རྡོ་རྗེ་འཆང་། པཎ་ཆེན་ཐམས་ཅད་
མཁྱེན་པ་མཆོག་གི་སྤྲུལ་སྐུ་དགུང་ལོ་བཅུ་གཉིས་བཞེས་པ་ན་བླ་བྲང་རྒྱལ་
མཚན་མཐོ་པོའི་གཟིམ་མཆུང་ཡིད་དགའ་ཆོས་འཛིན་དུ་བཞུགས་སྐབས།
ཕྱགས་ཆེན་ཞལ་སྔ་ནས་དང་ང་ཅག་དཔོན་སློབ་གཉིས་ཀྱིས་ཞུས་པ། རང་
རེ་བཀྲ་ཤིས་ལྷུན་པོ་བ་དཔོན་སློབ་རྣམས་ལ་དབྱིངས་ས་འདི་ཉིད་ཐུགས་མི་
དད་ཅིང་། གསུངས་ནས་ཀྱང་ཟློས་སྒོ་ ཀྱང་རྒྱང་དུ་རང་སོང་། དངོས་གཞི
༈ གོང་མ་ཐམས་ཅད་མཁྱེན་པ་ཞབས་པད་བརྟན་ཕྱིར་ ༈ རྒྱལ་བ་ཡབ་སྲས་
ལ་སོལ་འཛུག་གསོད་ཐབས་ཅི་ལ་ཡོད་ཀྱང་དབྱིངས་ས་འདི་ཉིད་ཐུགས་ཤིན་
ཏུ་ཚ་ཞིང་། གསུང་པའི་དགོངས་པ་ལེན་ཕྱོགས་ཞིག་མ་བྱུང་ན། དེ་རང་གི་
ལས་ཁུར་ཚོ་འཕྲུལ་དུ་ཟློས་བདེ་བ་རང་མ་བྱུང་དོགས་པ་ཡང་བཙམ་འདུག་ཚུལ་
ཞུས་པར། ཅུང་ཟད་གཅིག་སྤྱན་བཙུམ་ཏེ་བཞུགས། དེ་ནས་ཞལ་འཛུམ་
པ་མཛད་དེ། སྔེ་སྒྲིད་འདི་ཐུགས་ཚ་ཀྱང་ང་ཅག་ཚོའི་ལས་རྒྱུ་ཤོར་མི་ཡོང་།
འཕྲིན་ལས་ལ་ཡང་མི་གནོད། ༈ སྐུ་ཞབས་རྒྱལ་དབང་མཆོག་འདི་ཉིད་
སྔོན་ཚེ་ལོ་ཁྲི་ཐུབ་དུས་རྒྱལ་པོ་དོན་ཐམས་ཅད་འགྲུབ་པ་དང་། དེ་དུས་སྔེ་སྒྲིད་
འདི་རྒྱལ་པོ་གོ་ཆའི་བློན་པོ་ཏྲི་ཤུ་ཞེས་པར་སྐྱེས་པའི་དུས། ང་ཅག་བླ་མར་གྱུར་
པ་བློན་པོ་ནས་ལོག་ལྟ་ཐ་དད་དུ་གྱུར་པས། དེའི་ཤུགས་ཀྱིས་རང་ཅག་ཚོར་མི་

༄༅། །དད་པ་འབྱུང་བ་ཡིན་གསུངས། ནོན་པོ་དེའི་རྒྱུས་ཇི་ལྟ་བུ་
ཡིན་ཞུས་པས། སེམས་ལ་དྲན་པ་རྣམས་རིམ་གྱིས་བ་ཤེད་པ་ཡིན་
གསུངས་འདི་སྐད་ཅེས་བཀའ་སྩལ་ཏོ། །འཕགས་པ་ཐུགས་རྗེ་ཆེན་པོ་
ལ་ཕྱག་འཚལ་ལོ། །ཆོས་ཀྱི་རྒྱལ་པོ་དོན་ཐམས་ཅད་འགྲུབ་པ་ཞེས་བྱ་
བའི་རྣམ་ཐར་ལོ་རྒྱུས་གསང་བའི་ལུང་བརྗོད་པར་བྱའོ། །རྒྱ་གར་འཕགས་
པ་ཡི་ཡུལ་དུ་གདོགས་པ་ཟངས་གླིང་ཞེས་བྱ་བ་ན། ཆོས་ཀྱི་རྒྱལ་པོ་ཟླ་ལ་དེ་
ཤ་ཞེས་བྱ་བ་ཞིག་ཡོད་དོ། །དེ་ལ་རྒྱལ་པོ་ཤྲཱི་ཟླ་དྲའི་སྲས་མོ་ཀུན་བཟང་མ་
ཞེས་བྱ་བ་ཞིག་བཙུན་མོར་བསྟུས། དེ་ལ་ལོ་ཁ་ཡར་སོང་ཀྱང་སྲས་མ་འབྱུང་
སྟེ། མོ་མ་ཀ་རྩ་ཞེས་པ་རམ་མོ་ཕྱ་བྱས་པར་ཕྱིའི་རྒྱ་མཚོའི་གླིང་ལས་ཐོན་ཏེ།
ཀོ་ཤ་ཞེས་བྱ་བར་ལྷ་ཀླུ་ལ་མཆོད་པ་ཕུལ་གསོལ་བ་བཏབ་ན་སྲས་ཞིག་ཡོང་
བ་འདུག་ཟེར་ལུང་བསྟན་ཅིང་། སྲས་འབྱུང་ན་བྱ་དགའ་སྟེར་བ་ཞལ་གྱིས་བཞེས།
དེར་རྒྱལ་པོ་ཡབ་ཡུམ་བློན་འབངས་རག་བསྡུས་སྟོང་ཆོ་གཅིག་བཅས་རྒྱན་
ཆ་ལུགས་ཀྱིས་བརྒྱན། ལྷ་ཀླུ་མཆོད་པའི་ཆས་ཡོ་བྱས་གླང་པོ་ཆེའི་རྒྱབ་
ཁལ་མང་པོ་བཀལ་ཏེ་རྒྱ་མཚོ་ཕྱི་མའི་གླིང་ལ་ཕྱིན་ནོ། །དེར་རྒྱ་མཚོ་ལ་གྲུ་
དང་གཟིངས་ལ་སོགས་པ་མཚོ་སྟེང་དུ་ཞག་ལྔ་བཀལ་ཏེ། ལྷ་ཀླུ་གཞི་བདག་
གནས་པའི་ས་གཙང་ཀོ་ཤའི་གནས་དེར་ཞག་བདུན་གྱི་བར་དུ་དཀོན་མཆོག་
ལ་གསོལ་བ་བཏབ། དེ་བ་ཙ་མུ་ཏྲི་སོགས་ཆོས་སྐྱོང་ལ་གཏོར་ཚོགས་ཕུལ།

༄༅། །སྤྲེ་བརྒྱུད་ལ་མཆོད་གཏོར་བཤམས་ནས་བཞུགས་སོ། །ཞག
བདུན་གྱི་དགོང་མོ་རྒྱལ་པོའི་རྨི་ལམ་ན་ཨ་ཙར་དཀར་པོ་ཞིག་ཤེལ་ཕྲེང
ཐོགས་ཏེ་མདུན་དུ་ཡོང་ནས། བདག་གི་ཐུགས་ཀྱི་སྲས་སྤྲུན་རང་གཟིགས
དང་། འཇམ་དཔལ་གྱི་སྤྲུལ་པའི་རྒྱལ་བུ་གཉིས་བཙས་པ་ཡོད་དོ། །དགའ་བ
བསྐྱེད་ཅིག་གསུངས། རྒྱལ་པོས་ཁྱོད་སུ་ཡིན་ཞུས་པས། ང་ནུབ་ཕྱོགས
བདེ་བ་ཅན་གྱི་མགོན་པོ་འོད་དཔག་མེད་ཡིན་གསུངས། ཁྱོད་ཀྱི་སྲུང་མ་ཀྱང
གོ་ཤའི་གནས་བདག་དེ་ཕ་ཙ་སུ་ཏྲི་ཡིན་གསུངས། ཁྱོད་ཡབ་སྲས་གསུམ
གྱི་སྐྱེ་བ་ནས་ཚེ་རབས་ཀྱི་བསྲུང་མ་ཡིན་པས་མཆོད་གཏོར་ཡང་ཡང་ཕུལ
ཞིག་གསུངས། དེ་ནས་སྲས་ཡོང་བའི་རྨི་ལྟས་བཟང་པོ་བྱུང་གསུངས། རྗེ་ན
འབྲེལ་རྣམ་ཀྱང་འགྲིགས་ནས་ཕོ་བྲང་དུ་སོང་ངོ་། །དེ་ནས་ཟླ་བ་དགུ་ངོ་བཅུ
སོང་བའི་སྟག་གི་ལོ་ལ་སྲས་ཞིག་བཙུན་མོ་ཀུན་བཟང་མའི་མངལ་དུ་ཆགས
སོ།། །དེ་ཆགས་ནས་མི་རྟོག་གི་ཆར་འཇམ་འོད་ཀྱི་གུར་ལ་སོགས་པའི
མཚན་ལྟས་བཟང་པོ་ཡང་ཡང་བྱུང་ཞིང་། ཁྱད་པར་ལྷ་མོ་དྲར་དཀར་གྱིན
བཟའ་གསོལ་བ་ཞིག་གི་དུས་བཟང་བྱུང་རེས་ལ་ནམ་མཁའ་ནས་སྐུ་བྲུས
གསོལ་བ་ཀུན་གྱིས་མངོན་དུ་མཐོང་ངོ་། །ཟླ་གྲངས་ཞག་གྲངས་ཐིམ་ནས་སྲས
ཁྱད་པར་དུ་འཕགས་པ་མཚན་བཟང་པོས་སྤྲས་པ་ཐུགས་ཀར་ཧྲཱིཿ
ཡིག་འབུར་དོད་འོད་ཟེར་འཕྲོ་བ་ཞིག་འཁྲུངས་སོ། །དེར་ཆབ་འབབས་རྣམས

༄༅། །ལ་བཙས་སྟོན་རྒྱ་ཆེན་པོ་བཏང་། དཀོན་མཆོག་དང་ཡུལ་
ལྷ་ཆོས་སྐྱོང་ལ་གཏང་རག་གི་མཆོད་པ་ཕུལ་བྲམ་ཟེ་མཚན་མཁན་ཟླ་དྲ་ལ་བསྟན་
པས་སྤྲས་འདི་མཚན་དང་དཔེ་བྱད་ཀྱིས་བརྒྱན་པ་ངོ་མཚར་ཆེ་བ་འདི་ཧྲུ་བུ་ལོ་ཀ་
ཤྲཱི་རི་སྤྲུལ་པ་ཡིན་འདུག །ཁྱད་པར་འཕགས་པ་འདིས་རྒྱལ་པོ་སྐུ་ཆེ་མ་འཕོས་
པར་རྒྱལ་ས་འཛིན་པ་གཅིག་ཡོང་བ་འདུག །ང་ཅག་རྣམས་ཀྱི་བསོད་ནམས་ཨེ་ཐུ་
ཟེར། དེར་རྒྱལ་པོ་ཡབ་ཡུམ་གཉིས། འབངས་འཁོར་གཡོག་རྣམས་ཀུང་
དགའ། དྲུང་ཐུས། དར་འཕྱར། རོལ་མོ་བསིལ། དེར་རྒྱལ་པོ་དོན་ཐམས་
ཅད་འགྲུབ་པར་མཚན་གསོལ། མོ་མ་དང་མཚན་མཁན་ཟླ་དྲ་གཉིས་ལ་བྱ་
དགའ་ཆེན་པོ་གནང་བ་མོ་མ་ཀུང་བློན་པོར་བསྐོས་སོ། །དེ་ནས་རྒྱལ་ཁྲིམས་དེ
ཆོས་བཞིན་དུ་དར་བའི་དུས་སུ། རྒྱལ་པོ་དོན་ཐམས་ཅད་འགྲུབ་པ་ལོ་ལྔ་སོང་བ་
ཞལ་ནས་ཡིག་དྲུག་རང་གསུང་བ་ངོ་མཚར་བཞིག་ཡོད་པའི་དུས་སུ། །ཀུན་བཟང་
མ་དེ་སྐྱིད་གཞི་དྲག་པོས་བཏབ་ནས་གྲོངས། དེར་ཐམས་ཅད་སྨྱོ་ངན་དྲག་པོས་
ནོན། ཇོ་མོ་དེ་འདས་ལུང་པའི་ས་འཚུད་ཉམས་འགྲོ་ཟེར་དུ་དེར་བྱེད། དེ་ནས་
ག་ཤེགས་སྡོང་དཔག་ཏུ་མེད་པར་བྱས། དེ་ནས་ལོ་གཅིག་ཙམ་སོང་དུས་སུ་
བློན་འབངས་རྣམས་ཀྱིས་གྲོས་བྱས། ཇོ་མོ་དེ་འདྲ་ནི་འཛིག་རྟེན་ན་བཙལ་
ཀུང་མི་རྙེད། ཡིན་ཀུང་རྒྱལ་པོ་སྐུ་ན་གཞོན་ཞིང་ཇོ་མོ་ཞིག་འཚོལ་དགོས་ཟེར་
ཁ་འཆམ། དེ་ནས་ཟླ་བ་ཁ་ཤས་ཀྱི་བར་བློན་པོ་རྣམས་ཀྱིས་ཇོ་མོ་བཙལ་བས་

༄༅། །གྲུབ་ཐུབ་པ་ཞིག་མ་རྙེད་པའི་བར་ལ་ལུང་པར་མཆོད་སྟོན་གྱི
ལྷོད་མོ་ཆེན་པོ་ཞིག་ཡོད་པར་རྒྱལ་པོ་ཡབ་སྲས་གཉིས་གདན་དྲངས། དེར་མོ་···
ལུས་ཐོབ་ཚད་ཀྱང་ཁྲོམ་དེར་འདུས་པར་དེའི་ཁྲོད་དུ་ཕལ་པའི་བུ་མོ་པདྨ་ཅན་ཞེས
བྱ་བ་ལང་ཚོ་དང་ལྡན་པ་ཞིག་འདུག་པ་རྒྱལ་པོས་གཟིགས། དེར་བློན་པོ་ཞིག་ལ···
རྒྱལ་པོས་གསང་བའི་བཀའ་ཡི་མངགས། དེའི་སང་ཉིན་ཡབ་རྒྱལ་པོ་སྐྱིད་མོས
ཚལ་དུ་བྲུས་ཀྱི་རྫིང་བུར་སྐུ་ཁྲུས་ལ་འབྱོན་པ་དང་། བུ་མོ་པདྨ་ཅན་ནང་བློན་རྣ···
རིས་ཁྲིད་དེ་རྒྱལ་པོར་ཕུལ་བས་མཉེས། དེ་ནས་བཙུན་མོར་མངའ་གསོལ་བ···
སོགས་མེད་པར་རང་བཞིན་གྱིས་ཁབ་ཏུ་བཞེས། ཆབ་འབངས་རྣམས་འོས་མིན་གྱི
རྗེ་མོ་བཞེས་ཟེར་ཀློག་ལབ་ཀྱིས་རྒྱལ་པོར་བསྐུར་བ་འདེབས། དེ་ནས་བུ་མོ་པདྨ་ཅན
གྱི་རྨི་ལམ་ལ་མགོན་པོ་འོད་དཔག་མེད་ཀྱི་སྲས་ཡིན་ཟེར་བའི་ཨ་ཙ་ར་རལ་པ་ཁམ
སེར་རས་སེར་པོའི་ལྭ་བ་གྱོན་པ་ཕྱག་ན་འཁོར་ལོ་བསྣམས་པ་ཞིག་བྱོན་ལ······
ཞགས་འདེར་གཡོར་དགོས་གསུངས། སྤྱི་བོར་ཐིམ་པ་རྨིས། དེའི་རྒྱུ་མཚན་ཡབ
ལ་ཞུས་པས་བདག་ལ་བྱང་ཆུབ་སེམས་དཔའི་སྤྲུལ་པ་གཉིས་འབྱུང་བ་ཀོ་ཤའི···
གནས་སུ་ལུང་བསྟན་ཀྱང་ཡོད་ཅེས་མཉེས། གཙང་སྨྲ་དང་ལྡན་པ་གྱིས་ཤིག···
གསུངས། དེ་ནས་ཟླ་ཞག་ཐིམ་པ་དང་འོས་མིན་གྱི་རྗེ་མོ་དེ་ལ་ཡང་སྲས་མཚར
སྡུག་འོད་དང་ལྡན་པ་ཞིག་འཁྲུངས་སོ། །དེ་ནས་ཡང་བཙས་སྟོན་དང་དཀོན་མཆོག
ཆོས་སྐྱོང་ལ་མཆོད་པ་རྒྱ་ཆེན་པོ་དང་བཅས་མཛད་དོ། །དེ་ནས་བྲམ་ཟེ་ཟླ་དྲ་བོས་ཏེ···

f 6

༄༅། །བསྟན་པས་འདི་ཡང་བྱང་སེམས་ཀྱི་སྤྲུལ་པར་ཕྲ་ཆོམ་མི་ཤེས།
པས་གཞན་ནུ་དོན་ཡོད་ཅེས་མཚན་གསོལ་མ་ཐོག་ཏུ་མེ་ཏོག་གི་ཆར་དང་དངས······
གཡོས། དགེ་མཚན་གྱི་ལྟས་ཕུན་སུམ་ཚོགས་པ་བྱུང་། རྒྱལ་བུ་དེ་རེ་ཁྲིག···
ཞབས་ལ་འཁོར་ལོ་འབུར་དོད་འོད་ཟེར་གྱིས་སྤྲས་པ་མངོན་སུམ་དུ་ཡོད་དོ། །
བཙས་མ་ཐག་ཏུ་ཡུམ་ལ་ནུ་ཞོ་ཙམ་བཞེས་པ་ལས་མ་མ་རྣམས་ལ་ཡང་བློ་མི···
གཏོད་པ་ཇོ་ཇོ་རྒྱལ་བུ་དོན་ཐམས་ཅད་འགྲུབ་པའི་རྩར་ཉེན་མཚན་འཁོར་ཡུག་ཏུ་
བཞུགས་པ་ཡོད་དོ། །དེ་ནས་སྲུས་འདི་ན་སོ་གཞོན་པ་དང་སྐྱེ་མཆེད་མཛལ་བ་
ལ་དཔག་ཏུ་མེད། གསོལ་བ་ཡང་ཞེས་རེས་ཕྱུས་གཅིག་བྱས། གོས་གདན····
གཅིག་བྱས་གཟིམ་པ་གཅིག་ཡོད་དོ། །དེ་ནས་སྲུས་གཉིས་ཀ་ན་སོ་གཞོན་ཅིང་···
ནམ་ཞིག་ཙོན་པོ་བྱང་གི་རྩེ་ལ་གཟིགས་མོལ་བྱོན་ནོ། ཇོ་མོ་ཞག་ཁ་ཡར་པོ་བྲང་
གི་རྩེ་མོར་བྱོན་པའི་ཉིན་གཅིག་ཤར་ཕྱོགས་སུ་པོ་བྲང་གི་ཁ་བད་སྤྱན་ནས་གཟིགས་
པ་ན༑ ཤར་ན་རྩེད་མི་བྱེད་མཁན་ཁྲི་ཁྲུག་མང་པོ་འདུག་པར་རྩེད་མོར་འཁོར་
ཆོ་ལབ་ཆོལ་གཏམ་ངན་མང་པོ་སྨྲས་གིན་འདུག །དེའི་སེབ་ན་གཙོ་བོ་གྲོས་
བྱེད་མི་འགའ་ཡར་འདུག་པ་རྣམས་ཀྱིས། ངེད་རང་ཚོའི་རྒྱལ་པོ་ཆེན་པོ་
འདི་ལ་སྲུས་གཉིས་བཙས། འདིའི་རྒྱལ་སར་རྒྱལ་པོ་ཆེ་བ་འདི་བཀོད་པའི་
ངེས་ཡིན། ཨ་མའི་སྐབས་ཀྱིས་ཆུང་བ་འདི་ལ་རྒྱལ་ས་མི་ཐོས་ཟེར། །དེར་
ཡོད་པ་བྱིངས་ཀྱང་རྒྱལ་བུ་དོན་གྲུབ་འདི་ལ་ཨ་མ་ཀྱང་རྒྱལ་པོའི་སྲུས་མོ

༄༅། །ཡིན༔ དོན་གྲུབ་རང་ལ་སངས་རྒྱས་ཀྱི་མཚན་བཟང་ཀྱང་
ཡོད་པས་རྒྱལ་ས་སྤོང་ངེས་པ་ཡིན། རྒྱལ་བུ་དོན་ཡོད་མཚན་རྟགས་སོགས་
ངོ་མཚར་ལ་སྐུ་མཆེད་ཁྱད་ཆེར་མི་ཡོང་ཀྱང་། ཨ་མ་ངོས་མིན་ཡིན་ཙིང་གཙུང་
པོ་ཀྱང་ཡིན་པས་རྒྱལ་ས་མི་ཐོབ་ཟེར། གཏམ་དེ་ཐོས་པ་དང་བཙུན་མོ་སྙིང་མི་
དགའ་སེམས་པ་ཞིག་བྱུང་། དེ་ནས་ཕོ་བྲང་གི་རྩེ་ནས་ལྷོ་ཕྱོགས་སུ་བལྟས་པ་
ན༔ ལྷོ་ངོས་ཀྱི་ཐངས་ཆེན་པོ་ཞིག་ཡོད་པ་དེར་སྐྱེས་པ་ཐམས་ཅད་མདའ་རྒྱག
འཆོང་རྒྱག་རྡོ་མཆོགས་ལ་སོགས་ཙེད་གྱིན་འདུག །དེ་ནས་རྩེད་མོ་གྲོལ་བའི་
རྒྱལ་ཆང་འཐུང་བར་ཚོགས་པའི་གཏམ་ལ་རྒྱལ་པོ་དོན་འགྲུབ་ཡིན། རྒྱལ་པོ་
དོན་ཡོད་ནུ་བོ་ཀྱང་ཡིན་པས། རྒྱལ་ས་མི་ཐོབ་ཟེར་སྤྱར་ལྟར་སྙིང་ངོ། ། དེར་
བཙུན་མོ་རིག་སེམས་པ་ལ་ངའི་བུ་འདིས་རྒྱལ་ས་མི་ཐོབ་པ་འདྲ་བས་མཞིང་
ཆབ་འབངས་ཀྱིས་ཀྱང་ཁ་ལོག་ཡོད་པ་འདྲ་བས་མ་སྙིང་མི་དགའོ། །
ཡང་ཕོ་བྲང་གི་རྩེ་ནས་ནུབ་ཕྱོགས་སུ་ཕར་གཟིགས་པས་བུད་མེད་ཐམས་
ཅད་ཐག་ཐགས་རན་མ་ཐྲན་པ་ཞིག་འདུག །སྤྱ་དྲོའི་དུས་སྤྲིན་བལ་འཐག་
པ་ལྟར་འཕྱེད། ཉི་མ་ཕྱེད་ཡོལ་གཏམ་ཚོལ་མང་པོ་ལབ་པར་མི་རིགས་ས་མི
གཅིག་པ་ལས་ཐོད་སྒྱུ་སེང་ངེ་བ་མང་པོ་འདུག་དེར་གཏམ་སྙིང་ལ། དེད་རང་
གི་རྒྱལ་བུ་དོན་ཐམས་ཅད་འགྲུབ་པ་འདི་སྲས་ཆེ་བ་ཡིན། ཨ་མ་ཀྱང་རྒྱལ་
སྲས་ཡིན་པས་རྒྱལ་པོའི་ཁྲི་ཁང་གི་ཐོབ་ཡོང་། རྒྱལ་བུ་དོན་ཡོད་ཀྱི་ཨ་མ་

f 8

༄༅། །ཀུང་འོས་མིན་ཡིན། ཁོ་རང་ཀུང་གཙུང་པོ་ཡིན་པས་རྒྱལ་
ས་མི་ཐོབ་ཟེར་སློང་ངོ་། །ཡང་བཙུན་མོ་སེམས་བདེ་བ་སྐད་ཅིག་ཀྱང་མ་བྱུང་། ཕོ་
བྲང་གི་བྱང་ཕྱོགས་སུ་གཟིགས་པས་བུ་ཚ་ཕོ་མོ་རྩེད་མོ་བྱེད་པ་སྡོང་ཚོ་ཙམ་འདུས།
བུ་ཚ་ལ་ལས་ས་ཕྱུགས་ཀྱི་ཁྲི་བརྩིགས་ནས། རྒྱལ་བུ་དོན་གྲུབ་རྒྱལ་སར་འདོན་རྒྱུ་
ཡིན་ཟེར། ཕྲུ་གུ་གཅིག་གིས་དེའི་སྟེང་དུ་བསྡད་ནས་རྒྱལ་བུ་དོན་ཐམས་ཅད་
འགྲུབ་པ་ཡིན་ཟེར། ཕྲུ་གུ་མང་པོ་རྒྱལ་བུ་དོན་འགྲུབ་ཀྱི་བློན་པོ་ཡིན་ཟེར།
རྒྱལ་པོ་ལ་བསླབ་སྟོན་ཞུབ་འདྲ་བྱེད། ལ་ལས་འབངས་ཡིན་ཟེར་གོས་སྤུད་
ནས་ལག་པར་ཁྱེར་སྣེ་ནས་བཟུངས་ལ་གཏད་དེ་ཕྱག་རྟེན་འབུལ་བ་ཡིན་ཟེར།
ལ་ལན་རེ་ང་རྒྱལ་བུ་དོན་ཡོད་ཡིན་ཟེར་རྒྱལ་བུའི་ཁྲིའི་རྩར་རས་གཟན་གཏིངས་
ནས་སྡད། རྒྱལ་བུ་དོན་ཐམས་ཅད་འགྲུབ་པ་རྒྱལ་སར་ཐོབ་པའི་རྟེན་འབྲེལ
འཇི་མས་ལ་༥༥
བློན་པོ་རྣམས་ཀྱང་རྒན་གཞོན་ཕོ་མོ་ཐམས་ཅད་ཁ་འཆམ་པ་ཐོས་ཏེ། རྒྱལ་བུ་
དོན་གྲུབ་རྒྱལ་སར་བསྐོས་པ་ལ་ཐག་བཅད་ཅིང་། ཆབ་འབངས་ཀུན་བློ་མཐུན
ཁ་འགྲིག་འདུག་གོ །དེར་བཙུན་མོའི་བསམ་པར་རྒྱལ་བུ་དོན་ཐམས་ཅད་
འགྲུབ་པ་འདི་ལ་ཡུམ་མེད་ཀྱང་ཁོང་རང་གི་མིང་དང་རྟེན་འབྲེལ། འབངས་བློན
མོ་དང་བློན་པོའི་ལབ་བརྗོད་ལ་བལྟས་ན་རྒྱལ་ས་ཇོ་ཇོས་འཛིན་པ་འདུག །ངའི་བུ
འདིས་རྒྱལ་ས་མི་ཐོབ་པ་འདྲ། བུས་རྒྱལ་ས་མ་ཐོབ་ན་ཚེ་མ་ཁ་རྗེས་མི་ཡོང་བས་
རྒྱལ་བུ་འདི་མེད་པའི་ཐབས་ཤིག་བྱ་དགོས་བསམ་ནས་བསམ་ངན་གྱི་སྣང་བར་

༄༅། །ཕྲུར་རྡོ། །དེ་ནས་སྐབས་ཞིག་འགྲམ་པ་གཡས་སུ་བཙོག
འཚུག །གཡོན་དུ་རམ་བཙུགས་ནས་ལུད་པ་སྦྱོད་མར་ཤིག་ཕེ་བ་ཞིག་བྱས།
སུག་པ་དང་གླང་པོ་ཆེའི་ཀླད་པ་ཟླེས་ནས་སྒོ་དང་སྦྱིད་པ་མང་པོ་བྱས། སྐབས་ཁ
དེ་ནས་མར་བབ་ཕྱིན་པས། རྒྱལ་པོ་ཡབ་སྲས་སྐུ་མཁར་གྱི་འཁྲིས་དེ་ནས་སྐུ
གསུང་ཐུགས་རྟེན་ལ་བསྐོར་བ་མཛད་ཀྱིན་བཞུགས་པའི་ལམ་ཁ་དེ་ལ་སྐྲད་དེ
འགྱེལ་ནས་ལུད་པ་སྦྱོད་མར་ཤིག་པ་དེ་ཞལ་ལའི་སྟེང་ལ་ཕར་ལ་བྲ་ཆེལ་ལེ་གཏོར
ནས་ཨར་རྒྱ་ཕྱུ་ཟེར། རྒྱལ་པོས་ཁྱོད་ན་བ་དེ་ཅི་ཡིན་གསུངས་པས་ན་བ་ཡིན་ཟེར
ནས་ལན་མ་བཏབ། དེར་ཆོས་རྒྱལ་ཆེན་པོའི་ཐུགས་ལ་རྫི་མོ་སྤྱོན་མ་གྲོངས་པ
དེའི་སྟོབས་ཀྱིས་ཐུགས་ཆད་དེ་ཅི་དྲག ཅི་ཕན་ན་བསམ། ཐུགས་ཙབ་ཙབ
ཏུ་ཕྲུར་རྡོ། །དེར་མི་མས་མོ་བཏབ་སྨྲ་རྩིས་ཀྱང་ཕན་པའི་ཐབས་མ་བྱུང་། རིམ་གྲོ
སྟོབས་ཆེན་ལྟོ་ཆོག་སོགས་ཀྱིས་ཀྱང་མ་ཕན། མི་མ་མཐོང་ཤེས་ཅན་དེས་བཙུན
མོ་ཆེན་མོའི་བསྐྱུན་གཞི་ཀྱང་མ་ཡིན། སྦགས་པ་དང་རྩུས་པའི་བསྐྱུན་གཞི
ཀྱང་མ་ཡིན། ཐུགས་ལ་འཁྲུགས་ཆེན་པོ་བྱུང་བའི་བསྐྱུན་གཞི་གདའ་ལགས
ཟེར༑ རྒྱལ་པོ་ཀྱང་ཐུགས་ཁྲལ་གྱི་བསྐྱུན་གཞི་ཡོད་ལ་ཁད་བྱུང་། དེ་ནས
ཞག་གསུམ་སོང་བ་དང་བཙུན་མོ་རང་ལ་དྲིས་ན་ཨེ་དྲག་དགོངས། བུ་མོ་པདྨ
ཅན་ཁྱོད་ཀྱི་ནད་ལ་ཕན་པའི་ཐབས་འདྲ་ཁྱོད་རང་ལ་ཟེར་རྒྱུ་ཨེ་ཡོད། ཡོད་ན
བསྒྲུབ་པོ་གསུངས་སོ། །དེར་བཙུན་མོ་ན་རེ། ང་ལ་ཕན་པའི་ཐབས་འདུག་སྟེ

f 10

༄༅། །འདྲ་བྱས་པས་ཅི་ལ་ཡོང་། ང་འཆི་བ་རང་ཡིན་པས་ཁ་རོག་
འཇོག་པ་ཞུ་ཞུས་སོ། །དེར་རྒྱལ་པོས་ཁྱོད་ལ་ཕན་པའི་ཐབས་འདུག་ན་ལོས་བྱེད་ཅི
འདྲ་ཞིག་འདུག་པ་ཤོད་གསུངས། བཙུན་མོ་ན་རེ། དེས་ན་ཕན་ཐབས་ཞུས་པ
འགྲུབ་པའི་ཐབས་གང་འདྲ་ཞིག་ཀྱང་གནང་བའི་དམ་བཅའ་གནང་དགོས་ཟེར།
རྟེན་གྱི་དྲུང་དུ་རྒྱལ་པོས་དམ་བཅའ་མཛད་དོ། །དེ་ནས་བཙུན་མོས་སྨྲར་ཕན་རྒྱལ་པོ་
ཆེན་པོས་ཕན་པའི་ཐབས་འདི་བཞིན་གནང་མི་ཡོང་བས་མ་ཞུ་མ་ནུས། རང་རེའི
རྒྱལ་པོ་དོན་ཐམས་ཅད་འགྲུབ་པ་འདི། མི་མིན་བདུད་ཀྱི་ཆོ་འཕྲུལ་ཡིན་པར་འདུག།
འདི་བཅས་ནས་ཡུམ་ཀུན་བཟང་མ་ཀུན་གྱི་དཔེར་ལོས་པ་དེ་གྲོངས། བདག་ཀྱང
འཆི་བའི་གནོད་པ་སྤྲོ་ལ་གི་འདུག །བདག་རང་སྟོང་ཆུང་སྟེ། རྒྱལ་པོ་རང་ཀྱང་སྐུ
སྲོག་ལ་སྐྱོན་ཡོང་བའི་ལུང་བསྟན་རྨི་ལྟས་དང་བཅས་པ་བདག་ལ་བྱུང་། འདི་བགྲོང
ནས་བདག་ལ་སླེང་ཅིག་ཆེན་ན་ཕན་ཟེར། རྒྱལ་པོའི་སྐུ་སྲོག་ལ་ཡང་བགེགས་བཟློག
འགྲོ ༑ དེ་ལྟར་མིན་ན་ཕྱི་རི་རྒྱ་མཚོའི་གླིང་མི་མེད་ཀོ་ཤ་འི་གནས་སུ་སྤྱོལ་ན་ཐམས
ཅད་ལ་ཕན་པ་འདུག་ཟེར་ཞུས་སོ། །དེར་ཡབ་རྒྱལ་པོའི་ཐུགས་དགོངས་ལ། ངའི
ཆུང་མ་ཁྱེད་འཕགས་དེ་ཡོད་དུས་བུ་འདི་དཀོན་མཆོག་ལ་གསོལ་བ་བཏབ་བཀའ
སྐྱོང་ཆོས་སྐྱོང་ལ་མཆོད་གཏོར་བྱས་པས་སྐྱེན་པ་ཡིན། ཧཱུཾ་ཟེ་མཚན་མཁན་གྱི
ཞལ་ནས་ཀྱང་ངང་རང་མ་ཤི་བར་ལ་རྒྱལ་ས་འཛིན་པའི་ལུང་བསྟན། རང་རེའི
རྒྱལ་ས་མ་ཟིན་ན་གཞན་གྱི་རྒྱལ་ས་ཐོབ་དོན་ནི་མེད། མོ་མའི་ལུང་བསྟན་བྱུང་བ་ཀྱང

f 11

༄༅། །བདུད་ཀྱི་ལུང་བསྟན་མིན་ལས་ཆེ། བདག་ལ་ཟྲག་པ···
སོགས་པ་འདི་འདྲ་སྲིད་དམ་རྨི་ལམ་ཡིན་ནམ་མངོན་སུམ་ཡིན་དགོངས། །
ཅི་དྲག་ལ་ཐུག། རིན་ཀྱང་བཙུན་མོ་འདི་ལ་སྲས་གཅིག་ཀྱང་ཡོད་པས་མ···
ཡོད་དགོངས་ཏེ། རྒྱལ་པོས་ཁྱེད་ཀྱི་ནད་ལ་ཕན་ཀྱང་བུ་དོན་ཐམས་ཅད་འགྲུབ་
པ་འདི་བས་དན་མི་ཡོང་། སྔོས་སུ་སེམས་ཅན་ལ་གནོད་འཚོ་སྐྱངས་པ་
ཡིན་པས་བཀྲ་མི་ཤིས་པ་ཆེན་པོ་འདིང་། ཤི་ནས་ཀྱང་དམྱལ་བ་མནར་མེད···
གནས་སུ་སྐྱེ་འདི་འདྲ་ལས་མི་བྱེད། ཁྱོད་ཀྱི་ཟེར་བ་ལྟར་མཐའ་ལ་བསྒྲུས་
པས་ཆོག་ཟེར་ཞལ་བཞེས་ཤོ་རེ། །དེར་བཙུན་མོ་ཀྱང་དེའི་ཞལ་ཆས་ཁྱུང་
བ་དང་ནབ་ལས་བསྐྱེད་བྱུང་ངོ་། །ཡབ་རྒྱལ་པོས་འབངས་རྣམས་བསགས་
ནས་རང་པོའི་རྒྱལ་བུ་དོན་ཐམས་ཅད་འགྲུབ་པ་འདི་བདུད་ཀྱི་སྤྲུལ་པ་ཞིག···
ཡིན་པར་འདུག །བས་དན་མི་ཡོང་ཕོ་རང་དང་པོ་ལྟ་ལ་སྐྱོངས་པ་ཡིན་པས་
ཡུལ་དེ་ཁར་བཙུགས་གཏོང་བ་ཡིན། །དེའི་རྗེན་འབྲེལ་རྫོངས་ཆས་རྣམས་
གསོག་ཤིག་ཅེས་རྒྱལ་པོས་བཀའ་གནང་ངོ་། །བློན་པོ་རྣམས་ཀྱིས་རྒྱལ···
པོས་སྨྲ་བ་ལན་གཅིག་ཏུ་སོང་བས་ཞུ་མ་ནུས། ཕྱོག་ཏུ་བསྒྱུར་པ་ཚད་མེད་
པ་འདེབས། རྒྱལ་བུ་དོན་ཐམས་ཅད་འགྲུབ་པ་མཐའ་ལ་བཙུགས་ནང་
རེའི་རྒྱལ་སྲིད་འདི་ཡང་ལོད་དུ་འགྲོ། །བཙུན་མོ་འདི་ཞལ་ཕྱོགས་ལ་སོང···
བ་ཡིན་ཟེར་ཆབ་འབབས་ཀུན་མ་དགའ། དེར་རྒྱལ་པོ་དོན་འགྲུབ་རང་ལ···

༄༅། །དགའ་བ་ནམས་ཀྱིས་ཞུས་པ ། རང་རེ་ལི་བུ་ཙུན་མོ་འདི

རྒྱལ་བུ་ལ་ཐུགས་ལོག་ནས་རྒྱལ་པོ་ལ་སྐན་སྒྲ་ཕུལ། རྒྱལ་བུ་རང་བཀྲོངས···

པའི་གྲོས་དན······ལམས་ཀྱི་ཡོད་འདུག་ཟེར་ཞུས་པས། དེར་རྒྱལ་བུའི་

ཐུགས་ལ་བསད་པ་ལས་གང་ཡང་དྲག །བདག་གྲོས་འགྲོ་དགོངས་པོད་རང་

སྐུ་མཆེད་གཟིམས་མལ་གཅིག་ན་ཡོད་པ་དེ་ནས་པོད་རང་སྐུ་མཆེད་གཉིས···

ཟན་ལྷག་ཕྱུང་ཚོད་བས་གསུ། དེ་ནས་རྒྱལ་བུ་དོན་ཡོད་ལ་ཡབ་ཡུམ་གཉིས་

ནས་འབོད་མཁན་བཏང་ནས་གོས་རྒྱུང་ལྷམ་རྒྱུད་མདའ་རྒྱུད་ཨེ་རན་བལྟ·····

བར་ཤོག་གསུངས་གདན་འདྲེན་མི་བཏང་ཀུང་སྤྱུན་གཉིས་མཛེར་གྲགས་པས་

རྒྱལ་པོ་ཡབ་ཡུམ་གྱི་སར་མ་ཕེབས་སོ། །དེར་རྒྱལ་པོ་དོན་ཐམས་ཅད་འགྲུབ་

པས་རང་གི་གཙུང་པོ་ལ་བཀའ་སྩལ་པ། ཆབ་འབངས་རྣམས་ཀྱིས་ཨ་ཇོ་མཐའ་

ལ་བཙུགས་པར་འདུག །ཡབ་ཡུམ་གྱི་བཀའ་ཡང་གནང་ཕྱུང་བས། ཁྱེད་རང་

ཨ་ཇོ་རི་གླ་ལ་བཞུགས་པ་མི་དྲག་ཅེས་གསུངས་སོ། །དེར་ནུ་བོ་དོན་ཡོད་ན་རེ།

ཨ་ཇོའི་ མཐར་ལ་བཙུགས་པར་འདུག་ན་ཨ་ཇོ་རི་གླ་ལ་བདག་ཁྱེད་ཅིག་ཟེར་ནས་

ཨ་ཇོ་རི་གླ་ལ་འཁྱིལ་ལོ། །ཡང་ཨ་ཇོ་དོན་འགྲུབ་ན་རེ་བདག་མཐར་ལ་བཙུགས་

པ་ལ་བཟང་ཡོད་པ་མིན། ལམ་དུ་འཇིགས་པ་དུ་མ་ཡོད། ཟས་དང་སྐོམ་

མི་ཡོད། ཕྱིའི་རྒྱ་མཚོ་ཆེན་པོ་ལ་སྐྱུར་བ་ཡིན། ཁྱེད་རང་དེ་ལས་ཟས་ནོར་

གྱི་བདག་ཐུས་རྒྱལ་ས་བཟུང་བ་དྲག །ཨ་མ་རང་བུ་ཚ་གཞན་ཡོད་པ་ནི་མི་འདུག

༄༅། །ངང་རེ་གཉིས་ཀ་རྒྱལ་སྲུང་ན་ཡབ་རྒྱལ་པོའི་རིགས་བརྒྱུད་ཡང་
ཆད་འགྲོ། །དེ་ལས་ཕྱེད་རང་སྐུ་མཁར་གྱི་ནང་དུ་བཞུགས་ཤིག །བདག
གིས་ཁོང་ཡབ་ཡུམ་ཀྱི་བཀའ་ལ་མཉེས་ན་མི་ཡོང་བས་དགོངས་པ་དང་བསྟུན་
དགོས་བསད་ནབང་གླེ་ལོངས་ཞུས་པས། ནུ་བོ་རྒྱལ་བུ་དོན་ཡོད་ཀྱི་བཀྲུམས
ནས་ཨ་ཇོ་ལ་སྨྲུག་ལས་འདི་བྱུང་བས་རྒྱལ་བརྒྱུད་ཆད་ནའང་ཆད། ཤིག་སོན་
ཅི་བྱུང་ཡང་འུ་ཅག་གཉིས་སྤོངས་ནས་མཉམ་དུ་འགྲོ་གསུངས་ནས་ཨ་ཇོའི་
ཚ་ནས་གོམ་ཀྲང་ཡང་འགྲོ་མ་འདོད་དོ། །རྒྱལ་པོ་ཡབ་ཡུམ་གྱི་ཞལ་ནས་ནང་
པར་རྒྱལ་བུ་དོན་འགྲུབ་ཕྱིར་བཙུགས་དུས་བློན་པོ་རྣམས་ཀྱི་མ་ལག་གྱིས་ལ
ནུ་བོ་དོན་ཡོད་ནང་དུ་སྐོར་ཅིག་གསུངས་སོ། །དེ་ནས་གཟན་སྐར་ཚེས་གྲངས
ཙིས་ཏེ། རྒྱལ་བུ་མཐའ་ལ་བཙུགས་པའི་གྲབས་བྱས་སོ། །དེར་རྒྱལ་བུ
དོན་གྲུབ་ཀྱི་ཐུགས་ལ་བདག་ནུ་བོ་འདི་དང་འབྲལ་ཐབས་མི་འདུག །ངེད་གཉིས
སྤོངས་ཕྱིན་ཀྱང་ནུ་བོ་འདི་མེད་ན་རྒྱལ་པོ་ཡབ་ཡུམ་ཐུགས་ཁྲེལ་གྱི་བསྐྱུན
གཉིས་བྲིན་དོགས་འདུག །ངེད་གཉིས་ཁ་ཐུམ་ལ་ཤི་ན་རྒྱལ་སྤྱུད་ཆད་འགྲོ་བ
འདུག་དགོངས་ནས། ནམ་ཕྱེད་ལ་ཧ་ར་སྐྱེ་བཞེངས་པ་དང་ནུ་བོས་གསན་ནས་ཨ
ཇོའི་མགུལ་ལ་འཁྲིལ་ནས་ཉལ་ལོ། །ཨ་ཇོ་འགྲོན་ང་ཡང་འཁྲིད་ཟེར་ནས་དེ
ནུབ་འཚོན་མ་ཐུབ་བོ། །དེའི་དུས་སུ་ཨ་ཇོ་དགུང་ལོ་བཅུ་གསུམ་དང་གཅུང་
དགུང་ལོ་དྲུག་པའོ། །ད་དུང་ཐབས་ཤིག་བྱས་ཐོས་འགྲོ་དགོས་དགོངས་ནས

༄༅། །སྤྲུས་འགོར་བབས་གས་པའི་ཟླས་རྣམས་ཤཱ་རྒྱལ་ནང་དུ་
གཙུག་ནས་བཞག་གོ །ཞུ་ཁ་ཡར་གྱི་བར་དུ་རྗེ་རྗེས་འཆོན་པར་དགོངས་ཀྱང་།
ནུ་བོས་གསན་ནས་འགྲོ་མ་ཐུབ། ད་ཞིག་ང་ཟས་ཀྱང་མི་སྤྱོད་པ་ཡིན་པར་
འདུག་དགོངས། རྒྱལ་དང་སྲུར་བུ་འཛོམས་པའི་མི་ཚེ་ཉལ་ཀྲུང་ཉལ་ལ་
ཤཱཀྱ་ལ་དེ་སྤྲུག་པ་ལ་བཀལ་ནས་ཆོན་ནོ། །ནུ་བོག་ཙུང་གིས་ཀྱང་ཨ་རྗེ་ཆེན་
གྱི་དོགས་གོས་ལྷ་མ་མ་ཞུད་པ་ཡོད་པ་དེ་ལས་ལདས་ནས་ཨ་རྗེའི་རྗེས་ལ་
བསྐྱེགས་སོ། །ཨ་རྗེ་གར་འགྲོ་བའི་སར་བདག་འགྲོ་ཟེར་བཤུམས་ཀྱིན་
ཕྱིན་ནོ། །དེར་རྗེ་རྗེས་བུ་རང་སྤྲུག་རང་གིས་ཉེས་པ་ཕྱིད་འདྲ་ཡོད་པ། ཨ་
རྗེ་སྤྲུག་པའི་ཞོར་ལ་ནུ་བོ་ཀྱང་སྤྲུག་པར་འདུག་པས་སྙིང་རྗེ་གསུངས་ནས་
འཁྲིད་ཕྱིན་ནོ། །དེར་ཆོས་ཀྱི་བློན་པོ་རབ་བརྟན་དང་། ག་ཡ་ཧྲ་ར་གཉིས་
ཀྱིས་གསན་ནས་རྒྱལ་བུ་སྐུ་མཆེད་ཞབས་དུ་གདན་དྲངས་ཏུ་འབོད་ཀྱི་སྐྱེ་དགག་
འདོན། དེ་ནས་བློན་པོ་གཉིས་ཀྱིས་ཡབ་ཡུམ་གཉིས་ཀྱིས་མ་གསན་པར་
ཅུས༔ ཆིབས་རེ་དང་གླང་པོ་ཆེ་རྒྱབ་ཁལ་དང་བཅས་པ་ཕྱུལ། བླ་བ་
ཕྱིད་ཀྱིས་ལ་སྐྱེལ་ཐུངས་ཀྱི་གདན་འདྲེན་པ་ཀྱང་བཏང་ངོ་། །དེ་ནས་བློན་
པོ་གཉིས་ཀྱིས་རྒྱལ་བུ་སྐུ་མཆེད་ཕེབས་གདོང་སྐྱོན་ལམ་དུག་ཏུ་བཏབ་བོ།
དེ་ནས་ལམ་འགར་ཞིག་འདས་པའི་དུས་བླ་བ་ཕྱིད་སོང་བ་ན་གདན་འདྲེན་
པ་ཀུན་ཀྱང་ཕྱིར་སློག་གདན་འདྲེན་མི་གསུམ་ཀྱང་ལོག་མི་ཕོད་པའི་

༄༅། །སྡུག་བསྔལ་བྱུང་ཏེ་དུས་སོ། །དེར་རྒྱལ་བུ་དོན་འགྲུབ་
གྱིས༑ རིགས་དྲུག་སེམས་ཅན་ལས་འབྲས་སོ་སོར་སྨྱོང་། །འགྲོགས་
པའི་ཐ་མ་འབྲལ་བ་ཆོས་ཉིད་ཡིན། །འདུས་པ་མི་རྟག་ཚོང་དུས་མགྲོན་
པོ་འདྲ། །ཚེ་འདི་མི་རྟག་སོས་ཀའི་སྤྲིན་བུ་འདྲ། །ནོར་ནི་མི་རྟག་ཚོང་
པའི་ཟས་ནོར་འདྲ། །མི་རྟག་སྒོམ་པ་གནད་དུ་ཆེ་བའི་ཆོས། །ཁྱེད་རྣམས་
འདི་ནས་ཕར་ལ་ལོག་བྱོན་ཅིག །སླད་ནས་བློན་འབངས་རྣམས་དང་མཇལ་
བར་སྨོན། །ཞེས་གསུངས་སོ། །དེ་ནས་ཀུང་ཕོང་གསུམ་གྱིས་མ་ལོག་
པས༑ ༑ཡང་འདི་སྐད་ཅེས་གསུངས་སོ། །འདུས་བྱས་རྟག་པ་མ་ཡིན་
འཇིག་པ་ཡིན། །ལང་ཚོ་མི་རྟག་ནམ་མཁའི་འཇའ་ཚོན་འདྲ། །སྒྱུ་ལུས་
མི་རྟག་དཔྱར་ཁའི་མེ་ཏོག་འདྲ། །སྐྱེས་པའི་ཐ་མ་འཆི་བ་ཆོས་ཉིད་ཡིན། །
འདི་ནས་པར་ལོག་ཀུན་ལ་དེ་སྐད་གསུངས། །སངས་རྒྱས་ཞིང་དུ་མཇལ་
བའི་སྨོན་ལམ་འདེབས། །ཞེས་གསུངས་ནས་བྱོན་ནོ། །དེ་ནས་མི་གྲོང་
ཡོད་པ་རྣམས་ཀྱི་ཡུལ་དུ་ཆིབས་དང་གླང་པོ་ཆེ་རིམ་པར་བཙོངས་སྟེ་བྱོན། །
དེ་ནས་དཔག་ཚད་ལྔ་བརྒྱ་ཙམ་འདས་པའི་ཕ་རོལ་མི་གྲོང་སོགས་མེད་པའི་
བྱང་ཐང་བྱེ་མ་ལམ་མི་སྣང་པའི་སར་ཕེབས་སོ། །དེར་གཙུང་པོ་ཐང་ཆད་
ནས་ཨ་ཛིས་བྲུག་ནས་ཁྲིད་བྱིན་ཟན་ལྷག་རྣམས་བཞེས་བྱིན་བྱོན་ནོ། །
དེའི་དུས་སུ་རྒྱལ་པོ་ཡབ་ཡུམ་གཉིས་ནང་པར་ལངས་པ་དང་། རྒྱལ་བུ་མཐའ

༄༅། །ལ་བཙུག་པའི་གླབ་ཚར་ནས་རྒྱལ་བུ་གདན་འདྲེན་ལ······
བཏང་ངོ། །རྒྱལ་བུ་སྐུ་མཆེད་གཉིས་མཐོང་སན་མི་འདུག་ཟེར་རྒྱལ་པོའི
དྲུང་དུ་འབུལ་སོ། །དེ་ལྟར་མི་སྲིད་རང་རེའི་མངའ་འོག་རྣམས་ཀྱི་སར་ཡོད······
འགྲོ་བས་ཚོལ་ཞིག་གསུངས། བློན་པོ་རྣམས་ཀྱི་མངའ་འོག་ཚང་མ་སྐྱུལ···
ཞིང་བཙལ་བས་མ་རྙེད་དོ། །དེར་རྒྱལ་པོ་ཡབ་ཡུམ་གཉིས་ཀ་ཐུགས་ཁྲལ་ལ···
གདད། བཙུན་མོ་ཡང་ན་བཟུམ་ཡིན་པའི་ནངས་ཤེས་པ་ཞིག་བྱུང་། རྒྱལ···
འབངས་རྣམས་ཀྱང་རྒྱལ་བུ་སྐུ་མཆེད་འོ་རྒྱལ་ཞེས་དུས། བཙུན་མོ་དེ་ལ···
དེ་ཁ་ཕན་ཟེར་ཁ་ཅིག་ནས་སྔོན་པ་ལྟར་སྐུར་བ་འདེབས་མཁན་མང་པོ་བྱུང···
ངོ། །དེ་ནས་རྒྱལ་བུ་སྐུ་མཆེད་གཉིས་པོ་ས་བྱང་ཐང་དེ་ནས་དཔག་ཚད······
འགའ་ཞིག་འདས་པ། བྱང་ཐང་མི་སྐད་ཁྱི་སྐད་མེད་པ་འདྲེ་སྲིན་གཅན···
གཟན་གདུག་པ་ཅན་མང་པོ་ཚོགས་ས་ནས་སླེབས་སོ། །རྒྱལ་བུ་དོན་ཐམས···
ཅད་འགྲུབ་པ་བྱང་ཆུབ་སེམས་དཔའ་དེའི་སྐུ་དྲིན་གྱིས་སྐུ་མཆེད་གཉིས···
ལ་འདྲེ་སྲིན་གཅན་གཟན་རྣམས་ཀྱིས་ཀྱང་གནོད་པར··མ་གྱུར་ཏོ། །གླ···
བ་ཁ་ཡར་ཀྱི་བར་ལ་བྱང་ཐང་མི་མེད་ལ་འཁྱིམས་པས་ཨ་རྫོས་ཟན་རི་ལ་སྣ
རི་ཙམ་ཟོས། །གཙང་པོ་ཡུང་བསྐོར་རྒྱ་ཁམ་ཚད་ཙམ་མཆག་པ་བྱུང་ངོ། །
དེ་ནས་ཞག་ཁ་ཡར་སོང་བ་ན་ཆས་ཀ་ཐམས་ཅད་ཆད་ནས་ཅིདྲག་ལ་ཐུག །
སྡོད་རྐྱལ་པ་དེ་ཡང་གཏུབ་ནས་གསོལ་གྱིན་ཡོད། རྐྱལ་པ་ཚ་གྲོ་བའི་སྐབས

༄༅། །ཀྱིས་ཞལ་སྒོམ་པ་ལ་ཚད་མེད་པ་མེ་འབར་བ་ལྟ་བུ་བྱུང་
ངོ་༔ ༔བྱང་ཐང་ཡུན་རིང་ག་ཤེགས་པ་དང་སྨུག་གཟུགས་ཀྱི་སྟོབས་ཞན་པར་
གྱུར་ཏོ། །དེའི་དུས་སུ་སྐུ་ངལ་ཞིག་བརྟེན། ཤིང་གི་བསིལ་གྲིབ་ཞིག
ལ་བཞུགས་པས་ཤིང་ཏོག་ཨ་མྲའི་འབྲས་བུ་མང་རབ་འདུག་པ་ཨ་ཛོས
གཟིགས་པར་ཐུགས་དགྱེས་ཚོར་བྱུང་ངོ་། །ཤིང་ཏོག་དེ་ནས་མང་རབ་ཐུད
ཏེ་གཉིས་ཀས་གསོལ་བས་མི་ཏོག་སྙིང་པ་ལ་ཆུ་བྲུག་པ་ལྟར་བྱུང་ངོ། །དེར་
རྒྱལ་བུ་དོན་ཐམས་ཅད་འགྲུབ་པས་ཤིང་ཏོག་དེ་ནས་ལྷ་ཕྱག་ཏུ་བཞེས་ཏེ།
དཀོན་མཆོག་ལ་མཆོད་པ་ཕུལ། སྨོན་ལམ་འདི་བཞིན་བཏབ་བོ། བླ་མ་ཡི་དམ་
དཀོན་མཆོག་གསུམ། །མཁའ་འགྲོ་ཆོས་སྐྱོང་ཡུལ་ལྷ་གཞི་བདག་ལ། །
མཆོད་གཏོར་གཙང་མ་ཕུལ་ལ་དགྱེས་པར་མཛོད། །བཞེས་ནས་བདག་ཅག
གཉིས་ཀྱི་མགོན་སྐྱབས་མཛོད། །ལུས་ཀྱི་བར་ཆད་སྡུག་བསྔལ་བྱུང་གྱུར
ཀྱང་༔ ༔ཡབ་ཡུམ་བཀའ་བཞིན་སྒྲུབ་པའི་དམ་ཚིག་ཅན། །སྐྱིགས་དུས
རིགས་དྲུག་ཐར་པར་འདྲེན་པ་ཡི། །སྐྱབས་མགོན་བདག་ཅག་གཉིས་ཀྱིས་བྱེད་
པར་ཤོག །ཅེས་གསུངས་སོ། །དེ་ནས་ཕར་ལམ་ཞག་གཉིས་འདས་པན
ལུང་པ་ཆུ་མེད་པ་ཞིག་ཏུ་ཕར་ཕེབས་སོ། །གཙུང་གིས་འཛིན་མཐུབ་ཀྱང་ཨ་
ཛོས་རྒྱབ་ཏུ་རྒྱང་གྲགས་བདུན་ཅི་བར་དུ་ཙོན་ཀྱང་ཆུ་མ་བྱུང་ངོ་། །རི་སྒང་པོ་
ཆེའི་སྐྱོ་སྣ་འདྲ་བ་ཞིག་འདུག་པ་དེའི་རྒྱབ་ལ་ཆུ་ཨེ་ཡོད་བསམ། ཁྱེད་རང་འདི

༄༅། །རྒྱབ་སྤྲོད་ཅིག་ཨ་ཇོས་རྒྱ་མཚོ་ལ་དུ་འགྲོ་ཡོ་གྲ་གསུངས་པས་ཨ་ཇོས་
བདག་སྐྱུར་བ་ཡིན་པ་འདྲ་འདུག་གསུངས། དེར་རྒྱལ་བུས་ཇོ་སྐྱུར་བ་ཡོད་དམ་
རྒྱ་མ་བྱུང་ན་ང་ཅག་གཉིས་ཀ་འཆི་བ་འདུག་རྒྱ་འཚོལ་དུ་འགྲོ་བ་དུག་ཟེར་ཅིན་ནོ།།
དེ་ནས་ཕར་རྒྱང་གྲགས་གཅིག་ཙམ་ཕྱིན་ཀྱང་རྒྱ་མ་བྱུང་། རི་གདོང་དེར་སྤྲེལ་བ་གྲང་
ཡོད་པ་དང་གཙང་གེས་སྤྲེ་རེ་ཨ་ཇོ་ལ་གཟིགས་ཀྱིན་བཞུགས། ཨ་ཇོས་ཕྱི་མིག་
གཟིགས་ཀྱིན་ཕྱིན་པས་རི་གདོང་གི་སྟེ་ལ་སྤྲེལ་བ་དང་། ཨ་ཇོ་ཟེར་སྐད་ཆེན་
པོ་བྱུང་སྟེ། ཐེན་ཏེ་གཟིགས་པས་གཙང་པོ་ཕུབ་སྟེ་འཁྱིལ་བ་གཟིགས། དེ་
མ་ཐག་ཏུ་ཨ་ཇོས་ལུས་མཆོག་ས་པར་བསྐྱལ་ཏེ་ཕྱིན་པས། གཙང་པོའི་རྩར་
སླེབས་དུས་ཞལ་འབྱུག་རྒྱུ་མེད་པར་སྐྱོན་རྩང་ཟད་གདང་ཞལ་དབུགས་མ་ཆད་
ཙམ་འདུག་པ་དང་། དེར་ཨ་ཇོས་པད་དུ་སླང་སྐྱུར་གས་བསྐོལ་ནས་ཧ་ལ་སྐྱུར་
ཞལ་ནས་མཆིལ་མ་རྩང་ཟད་གཙང་པོའི་ཞལ་དུ་བླུག་པས་རྩང་ཟད་གསོས་
པར༔ ཨ་ཇོས་བདག་གཉིས་ཀྱི་སྡུག་བསྔལ་འདི་འདྲ་བ་རིགས་དྲུག་སེམས་
ཅན་རྣམས་ཀྱིས་མྱོང་བར་མ་གྱུར་ཅིག །སེམས་ཅན་ཀུན་གྱི་སྡུག་བསྔལ་
ཐམས་ཅད་བདག་ཅག་སྐྱུན་གཉིས་ཀྱིས་མྱོང་བའི་མཐར་སེམས་ཅན་ཐམས་
ཅད་འདྲེན་པའི་དེད་དཔོན་དུ་གྱུར་ནས་སེམས་ཅན་གྱི་དོན་འབའ་ཞིག་བྱེད་
པར་གྱུར་ཅིག །ཅེས་སྨོན་ལམ་བཏབ་ཅིང་བ་ལུམ་མོ། །དེར་གཙང་གེས་
ཀྱང་སྐྱུན་རྡེག་གེ་གཟིགས་ནས། ཨ་ཇོ་རང་རེ་གཉིས་སྐྱེ་བ་ནས་ཚེ་རབས་

༄༅། །སྒྱུ་འཕྲུལ་བར་མི་འབྱུང་ང་དེ་རིང་ཨ་ཇོ་འབྲོན་དུས་ནམ་
མཁའ་འ་ནས་སྐྲ་ཞིག་ཁྲང་བྱུང་བས་ཁྲུང་ཐད་སེམས་མ་བདེ། ལྷ་གླུ་མ་རེ་ལྷུང་
བསྟན་ཁྲང་ཡོད། དནེ་བདག་འཆིབ་ལས་མི་འདུག་ན་འང་བདག་གི་ཨ་···
ཇོ་འདི་སྡུག་བསྔལ་མྱོང་བར་མ་གྱུར་ཅིག །ངེད་སྐུ་མཆེད་གཉིས་མཇུར་དུ་
མཇལ་བར་ཤོག་ཅིག །ཅེས་སྨོན་ལམ་བཏབ་བོ། །དེའི་དུས་དེ་མ་ཐག་ཁྱི་···
ཀ་ལ་པིངྐ་གཉིས་བྱུང་སྟེ། བདག་ཅག་གཉིས་མ་འོངས་པ་ཁྱེད་སྐུ་མཆེད་
གཉིས་ཀྱི་ཞབས་ཏོག་འཕྲིན་ལས་པར་གྱུར་ཅིག །ཅེས་སྨོན་ལམ་བཏབ་
བོ༔ ༔དེ་ནས་ཡང་ཁྱི་ཀ་ལནྡ་ཀ་གཅིག་བབས་བྱུང་བས་ཁྱེད་སྐུ་མཆེད་····
གཉིས་ཀྱི་ཞབས་ཏོག་ཏུ་འགྱུར་བའི་སྔོན་གྱི་རྣམ་ཐར་མ་ལུས་པ་དྲན་ཏེ་····
བསྟན་བཅོས་བརྩོམ་པ་ལ་མཁས་པའི་པཎྜི་ཏར་གྱུར་ཅིག་ཟེར་རོ། །ཡང་
ཁྱུ་གཅིག་བྱུང་སྟེ། ཆོས་ཀྱི་རྒྱལ་པོ་དོན་འགྲུབ་སྐུ་མཆེད་གཉིས་ཀྱི་རིམ་གྲོ་
པ་མངོན་ཤེས་སྐད་གཉིས་སྨྲ་བ་གཅིག་ཏུ་གྱུར་ཅིག །ཅེས་སྨོན་ལམ་བཏབ་
བོ༔ ༔དེ་ནས་དེ་མ་ཐག་པར་གཞུང་གི་དབུགས་ཆད་དོ། །དེ་ནས་ཨ་ཇོས་སྔན་
ནས་བཟུངས་ཏེ་བཤུམ། ངཅག་ཨ་ཇོས་ནུ་བོ་སྐྱིལ་ཟིན་ཞེས་ཞལ་གཏུགས་
ཏེ་མང་དུ་བཤུམས་སོ། །དེ་མ་ཐག་གཞུང་པོའི་སྐུ་གདུང་གི་ཞབས་སུ་སྨོན···
ལམ་འདི་བཞིན་བཏབ་བོ། །ངཅག་གཉིས་འབྲལ་མེད་གཅིག་ཡིན་པ་ལ་ད་
ངཅག་གཅིག་པོར་ལུས། ཕ་མ་རྒྱལ་སྲིད་དང་བཅས་པ་ལེ་གསེབ་ནས་མར་

f 20

༄༅། །ཀྱེ་དཀྱིལ་ནས་སྐྱུ་བརྟེན་པ་བཞིན། བདག་ཅག་སྐྱུན་
གཉིས་མཐའ་ལ་འཁོར་བའི་མཐར་བདག་གཅིག་བྱུར་ལུས་ངོ་ཤེས་པས་
དང་གནམ་ལས་མེད། ཚེ་སྔོན་མི་དགེ་བ་བསགས་པའི་རྣམ་སྨིན་ཅི་འདྲ་
ཞིག་ཡིན། བདག་རང་ཤིན་ནས་ནུ་བོ་ལུས་ཆོག་པ་ཨང་ཟེར་སྐྱེ་ངག་འདོན་བོ།།
འོན་ཀྱང་འདུས་བྱས་མི་རྟག་པའི་ཆོས་ཉིད་འདི་ག་རང་ཡིན། །བདག་ལ་ཚེ་
སྔོན་མའི་བླ་མ་ཡི་དམ་སྲུང་མ་ཡོད་ན་ཚེ་འདིར་ལུས་མ་བོར་བར་ང་ཅག་
སྤྱུན་གཉིས་འཕྲད་ནས་ཕ་མ་རྒན་མགོ་དང་མཇལ་བར་ཤོག་ཅིག །མི་དགེ་
སྡིག་པའི་ལས་རྣམས་སྤོང་བའི་བློ་དང་ལྡན་པར་ཤོག་ཅིག །དཔེ་འདི་ལ་
བསམ་ནས་ཟས་སྣོམ་རང་ལ་གང་ཡོད་སྦྱིན་པའི་ཕྱོགས་སུ་གཏོང་ནུས་པ་
ཞིག་ཏུ་གྱུར་ཅིག །ཀུན་ལ་ཡོང་ངེས་པ་མི་རྟག་འཆི་བ་འདི་ཐག་རིང་པོ་ན་
མི་འདུག་པས་མི་རྟག་འཆི་བ་དྲན་པར་ཤོག་ཅིག །ནམ་ཕྱུགས་བྱང་ཆུབ་
ཀྱི་འབྲས་བུ་ཐོབ་ནས་བདག་ཅག་སྐྱུན་གཉིས་ཀྱི་བསྟན་པ་རིན་པོ་ཆེ།
སེམས་ཅན་ཐམས་ཅད་ཀྱི་མགོན་སྐྱབས། སྟོན་པའི་རྒྱལ་ཚབ་དམ་པ་ཐོབ་
པར་གྱུར་ཅིག །ཅེས་སྨོན་ལམ་དཔག་ཏུ་མེད་པ་བཏབ་ཏེ་དར་ཅིག་ཏེ་ངང་
འཛིན་ལ་བཞུགས་སོ། །དུས་དེར་བྱ་དང་གཅན་གཟན་གྱིས་བསྐོར་བ་བྱེད།
ས་རྣམ་པ་དྲུག་ཏུ་གཡོས། མེ་ཏོག་གི་ཆར་དང་ལྷས་རོལ་མོ་དཀྲོལ་ལོ། །
དེ་མ་ཐག་སྤྲ་ཞིག་དང་སྤྲེའུ་ཞིག་བྱུང་སྟེ། དེ་གཉིས་ཀྱིས་ཀྱང་བསྐོར་བ་བྱས

f 21

༄༅། །དེ་ཞབས་འབྲིང་པར་སྨོན་ལམ་བཏབ་པས། སྟག་ཞིག་ཕྱུང་
སྟེ་ཀོང་གཉིས་སྨོན་ལམ་དེ་ལྟར་འདེབས་པ་མི་རང་བཞིན་པར་གསོལ་བ་བཏབ
པས་ཅི་ལ་ཕན་བསམ་ལོག་ལྟ་ཞིག་སྐྱེས་སོ། །དོན་ཀྱང་ཁོང་གཉིས་ཟེར་བ
བཞིན། ཁའི་མཛེས་མཚོན་དུ་བདག་ཅག་ཀྱང་ཁྱེད་སྐུ་མཆེད་གཉིས་ཀྱི
ཞབས་འབྲིང་དུ་སྐྱེ་བར་ཤོག་ཅིག་ཟེར། དེ་ནས་ཏིང་ངེ་འཛིན་སད་ནས་ད་རྒྱུད
ཀྱང་མ་ཕན་པ་འདུག་དགོངས་གཙུང་གི་གདུང་དེ་རྒྱབ་ཏུ་འཁུར། ལམ་ལྷུང
བརྒྱད་བརྒལ་ས་ར་རི་སྣེད་ཞིག་ཙནྡན་སེང་ལྡེང་ཤུག་པ་ཨ་རུ་ར་སོགས་ཀྱི
ནགས་ཚལ་དང་། ལོ་མའི་ཆུ་རྒྱུན་འབབ་པའི་ས་གཙང་བྲག་ཕུ་སྒྲིབས་ཡོད
པའི་སར་ཙནྡན་གོར་ཤའི་སྡོང་པོ་གུར་ཕུབ་པ་འདྲ་བ་ཞིག་འདུག་པ་གཟིགས
པས་ཐག་ཉེར་སོང་དུས་ཀེ་བའི་ཐད་དུ་འཛེར་ཁ་དོག་སྣ་ལྔའི་གུར་ཕུབ་པ
ལྟར་གྱུར་འདུག་པར་དེ་ལ་གཟིགས་ཏེ་ཕྱིན། ཙནྡན་གོར་ཤའི་བསིལ་གྲིབ
ཀྱི་ངོགས་སུ་སེམས་ཅན་གྱི་གནོད་པ་མི་འབྱུང་བར་བྱས། གཡམ་སྒྲོམ་ལེགས
པར་བཟོས་ཏེ་གཙུང་གི་གདུང་བཞག །ཙནྡན་གྱི་བསིལ་གྲིབ་དང་ཟིལ་པའི་རྒྱུ
ཐིག་ཡོད་པར་བྱས་བཞག་གོ །དེ་ལ་ཆགས་ཀྱང་འཚོ་བས་གདུགས་གཅན
གཟན་གྱི་ཡུལ་དུ་སོང་བས་བཞུགས་མ་ཐུབ་ནས་གཡམ་སྒྲོམ་དེ་ནམ་མཐོང
གི་བར་དུ་འབྲལ་མི་ཕོད་པའི་སྤྱན་ཆབ་དང་བཅས་མིག་བལྟ་བཞིན་ཕྱིན་ནོ། །རྒྱལ
ཏུ་དེ་ནས་ཀྱང་རི་སྣ་བཅུ་གསུམ་བརྒལ་ནས་ཕྱིན། དེ་ནས་ཞག་བདུན་སོང་བ

༄༅། །དང་ལྷའི་དབང་པོ་བརྒྱ་བྱིན་གྱིས་དྲང་སྲོང་ཞིག་ཏུ་སྤྲུལ་
ནས་ཤི་གསོལ་ཀྱི་སྨན་ཐུམ་བུ་ཞིག་ཁྱེར་ནས་བྱོན་ནོ། །ལྷ་ཚངས་པས་
བྲམ་ཟེ་ཞིག་ཏུ་སྤྲུལ་ནས་ཀ་ཤི་ཀའི་དར་གྱི་ན་བཟའ་ཞིག་བསྣམས་ཏེ་རྒྱལ་
བུ་དོན་ཡོད་ཀྱི་སྐུ་གདུང་གིས་རབ་ཙེན་པ་དང་གཡམ་སྒྲིམ་གྱི་ནང་དུ་ཙོན་གྱི་ཟེལ་
པ་བྱུང་བའི་སྐྱོབས་ཀྱིས་སྐུ་གདུངས་ཉམས་མ་མ་སྐམ་གསོན་པོ་ལྷར་མཛེས
དང་ལྡན་པར་འདུག །དེ་ནས་དྲང་སྲོང་དེས་ཙཱུན་གྱི་ཐང་ཆུལ་ག་བུར་གྱི་
ཁ་ཚར་བཏབ་ཏེ། ཞལ་དུ་ཐེང་གཉིས་བླུར་མས་ཞུས། དེ་རྗེས་ཤི་
གསོལ་ཀྱི་སྨན་སྦྱིན་ཏེ། ཐུར་མས་ཞལ་དུ་སྒྲོན་པས་དྲོད་སྐྱེས། ཡང་
ཐུན་གཅིག་སྒྲོན་པའི་སྐབས་ཐུགས་ཀྱི་དྲན་པ་སྐྱེད་དོ། །དེ་ནས་ཐུན་གཅིག་
ཞལ་དུ་སྒྲོན། ཐུན་གཅིག་སྐུ་ལ་བྱུགས་པས་བཞེངས་ཐུབ་གསུངས། །འཚོན་
ཐུབ་པ་བྱུང་ངོ། །བྲམ་ཟེས་ཀ་ཤི་ཀའི་དར་གྱི་ན་བཟའ་ཕུལ། དེར་རྒྱལ་བུ་དོན་
ཡོད་གྲིས་ཁྱེད་གཉིས་སུ་ཡིན། ཡུལ་གང་ནས་བྱོན། བདག་གི་ཨ་ཇོ་
ཐུགས་རྗེ་ཅན་དེ་མིན་པར་འདུག །ཁྱེད་གཉིས་ཀྱི་གཟིགས་སུ་ཞོ་གསུངས །
དེར་དྲང་སྲོང་གིས་བདག་ལྷའི་དབང་པོས་ཁྱེད་ལ་ཤི་གསོལ་ཀྱི་སྨན་སྐྱེར་བར་
བཏང་བ་ཡིན་ཟེར། བྲམ་ཟེས་ལྷ་ཚངས་པས་ཁྱེད་ལ་ན་བཟའ་འབུལ་དུ་
བཏང་བ་ཡིན་ཟེར། ཁྱེད་ཀྱི་ཨ་ཇོ་རི་ལུང་བཙོ་བརྒྱད་བརྒལ་ཏེ་སོང་ཞེས་
ཞུས་སོ། །དེར་རྒྱལ་བུས་ཁྱེད་གཉིས་བདག་ལ་བཀའ་དྲིན་དུ་གྱུར་གསུངས

༄༅། །ཕྱག་འཚལ་མཛད། ཁྱེད་གཉིས་ལྷ་ནས་མི་ཡུལ་ས····
སྐྱེད་དུ་འབྱོན་པའི་ནུས་མཐུ་འདི་ལྷ་བུ་ཡོད་པ་ལ། བདག་གི་ཨ་ཇོ་དང······
མཇལ་བའི་ཐབས་མཛད་དུ་གསོལ་གསུངས་པས། ཨ་ཇོ་འཚོལ་དུ····
བདག་གཉིས་འགྲོ་ཡི་གསུངས་ཏེ་རྒྱང་གྲགས་གཅིག་ཙམ་ནས་གཉིས་ཀ····
འཛར་ལྷུར་ཡལ་སོང་ངོ་། །དེར་རྒྱལ་བུ་དོན་ཡོད་ཀྱི་ཐུགས་ལ་ཡུལ་འདི་ལ་བྱ·
དང་གཅན་གཟན་རི་དྭགས་མ་གཏོགས་མེད་པ་ལ། ང་རེས་དྲང་སྲོང་དང
བྲམ་ཟེ་གཉིས་རང་རེའི་ལྷ་སྲུང་གི་སྤྲུལ་པ་མཛད་པ་ཡིན་འདུག །ད་ཤིང་
ཏོག་ཞིག་འཐུ་དགོངས་པ་ལ། དེ་ཁའི་སྤྱིལ་པ་སྐྱེ་ཞུ་ཞིག་གི་ཤིང་ཏོག་མང
དུ་སྤུལ་ཞིང་ལབ་བ་རྫམ་ཤེས་ནས་ནགས་སེབ་ཏུ་ལོག་སོང་ངོ་། །དེ་ནས
ཟས་སུ་ཤིང་ཏོག་བཙལ། སྐྱེམ་དུ་ཆུ་བཏུང་། གོས་སུ་ཤིང་ལོ་གྱོན། ཤིང་
ཏོག་བཞེས་རེས་ལ་ཨ་ཇོའི་ཟས་ཕུད་ཟེར་རྗེ་ལེ་བསྐྱེད་བཞག་ནས་བདག
གི་ཨ་ཇོ་མཆེད་ཅིག་ཟས་སྐལ་འདི་ན་ཡོད་དོ་གསུངས། ཤུམས་ཤིང····
སྐྱི་ངག་འདོན་ཀྱིན་ཨ་ཇོ་གང་ན་བཞུགས་ཡོད་པ་གསུངས་རི་སུལ་ནགས
སེབ་ཐམས་ཅད་ཉིན་རེ་བཞིན་ཙལ་བར་བྱོན། དེ་དང་ཨ་ཇོ་དང་མ་མཇལ····
བའི་སྡུག་བསྔལ་དང་ཨ་ཇོ་རེ་སྣང་ཐམས་ཅད་ལ་འཚོལ་གྱིན་ཡོད་དོ། །
དུས་དེར་རྒྱལ་བུ་དོན་ཐམས་ཅད་འགྲུབ་པས་རི་སྣ་ཆེ་བ་བཙུ་གསུམ་བརྒྱལ····
བའི་ལམ་ཁ་རི་ཐང་མཚམས་ཞིག་ཏུ་སྐུ་ངལ་གསོས་ཏེ་བཞུགས་པ་ན། དེ་ཁའི

༄༅། །ཐུབ་རི་མཐོ་ལ་ཤ་ཆེ་བ་སྐེད་པ་མན་ནགས་འཐུག་པོ་
སྐེད་སྟོད་གཡའ་དང་སྤང་འདྲེས་པ་ཞིག་འདུག་པའི་ལྷོའི་ཕྱོགས་གཡར་
སྤང་གི་མཚམས་སྣུམ་ནགས་ཚལ་མཚམས་ན་དར་ལྕོག་ཞིག་སྐྱ་ལྷེབ་པེ་
གཟིགས་སོ། །དར་ལྕོག་དེ་ཀ་ཡོད་པའི་ཐད་ཀར་ཕྱིན་ཏེ། འདི་ཕྱོགས་ན་
གྲོང་འབྲོག་འདྲ་ཞི་མི་འདུག་སྙམ། དར་ལྕོག་ལ་བལྟས་ན་མི་ཞིག་ཡོད་པ་
ཐག་ཆོད་དགོངས་ནས་རིམ་གྱིས་ཕྱིན་ཙ་ན། ནགས་དེའི་མཚམས་རི་སྐེད་ལ
འཕྱོར་དུས་མིས་ཁྱིམ་པའི་རྐང་རྗེས་ཐལ་ལེབ་གཟིགས་དེ་ལ་ལྟས་ཏེ་ཕྱིན
ནས། །འདིར་རི་ཁྲོད་དགོན་པ་ཞིག་ཡོད་པ་འདྲ་དགོངས། དེ་ནས་ནགས་
ཟད་མཚམས་ཀྱི་སྤང་གི་ལོགས་ནགས་ཐུག་པོ་ཡོད་པར་འཕྱིན་པ་དང་།
དར་ལྕོག་ཡོད་པའི་འོག་ཙམ་གྱི་རི་སུལ་ཞིག་གི་ཐད་ན། ཏིང་ཤག་གི་སྒྲ
སྙང་ངེ་བ་གསན་པ་དང་དགོན་པ་ཞིག་ཡོད་པ་ཐག་ཆོད་དགོངས་དགེས
ཚོར་ཆེན་པོ་བྱུང་། དེར་ཡར་འཛེགས་ཏེ། ཕེབས་པ་ན་རི་སུལ་དེའི
འགོར་ཆུ་མིག་ཞིག་འདུག་པ། དེའི་ཟུར་དགེ་སློང་བསྐྱེས་ཉམས་ཅན་
ཤ་ནའི་རས་ཀྱི་ཆོས་གོས་གསོལ་བཞིན་ཆུ་མིག་དེའི་ འགོར་གཏོར་
མ་གཏོང་གིན་བཞུགས་འདུག་གོ །བླ་མ་ལ་རྒྱལ་བུས་ཕྱག་ཕུལ་བས་
བླ་མའི་ཏིང་ངེ་འཛིན་ལས་དེ་གཟིགས་བྱུང་བ་དང་། རྒྱལ་བུས་ཕྱག་མང་
དུ་མཛད། དེར་རྒྱལ་བུ་ཁྱང་ཐང་རི་སྐུང་མང་པོ་ཕྱུལ་བ་དང་གསོལ་བ་མ

༄༅། །འཕོངས་ལྷག་པར་ནུ་བོ་གྲོངས་པའི་མྱ་ངན་གྱི་དབུ་སྐྲ
གཟིངས། ཤ་ལྷགས་རིད་ན་བཟའ་ཐམས་ཅད་རྒྱལ་པོར་ཕྱུར་ཏེ་འདོམས
ཀྱང་སྤྱོད་མི་ཐུབ་པ་ལྟར་གྱུར་ནས་ཡི་དྭགས་བསྣན་ལྟར་འདུག་པ་བླ་མས
གཟིགས། བླ་མའི་མངོན་ཤེས་ཀྱི་རྒྱལ་པོ་ཞིག་གི་ཕྱུས་མཐར་ལ་འཁྱམས་པ
ཞིག་ཡིན་པ་འདྲ་དགོངས་ཀྱང་མ་མཆིན་པའི་རྒྱལ་མཛད། ཁྱོད་ཡི་དྭགས
ཡིན་ནམ་མི་ཡིན་གསུངས་པར་རྒྱལ་བུས་བདག་ཡི་དྭགས་མིན་ལགས། རྒྱལ
པོའི་བུ་དར་རྒྱུད་འབྱུང་བ་ཞིག་མཐར་ལ་འཁྱམས་པ་ཞིག་ཡིན་ལགས་ཞུས། ད
གང་དུ་འགྲོ་གང་དུ་སྡོད་རྒྱུ་ཡིན་གསུངས། དེར་རྒྱལ་བུས་བླམ་ལ་ཕྱག་མཛད།
བདག་གར་འགྲོ་གར་སྡོད་ཀྱི་གནས་མེད་བླམ་བཞུགས་ས་མ་གེའི་ཀླུང་ནས
དར་ཕྱོག་མཐོང་ནས་ཡོངས་པས། བླ་མའི་སྒྲུབ་གཡོག་ཞུས་ཆོག་པ་ཐུགས
ལ་འདོགས་ཞུས་པས། བླ་མའི་ཐུགས་ལ་སྙིང་རྗེ་དཔག་ཏུ་མེད་པ་ཞིག་སྐྱེས
ཏེ༔ དོན་འུ་ཅག་གཉིས་ནང་དུ་འགྲོ་ཡོ་གསུངས་ནས་ཕྱིན །དེ་ཁའི་ཕར་ལོག
རྗེ་ཡི་ཕ་བོང་ཐོག་ཚད་གཉིས་ཙམ་ཡོད་པ་ཞིག་གི་ཤར་ལོགན། མགོན་པོ་འདིང
དཔག་མེད་དང་རིགས་གསུམ་མགོན་པོ་རང་བྱོན་བྱེས་པ་ལོ་བརྒྱད་ཙམ
འཁུར་དོད་ཡོད་པའི་ཐང་བྲག་ཕུག་ཞིག་གི་མདོར་འཛག་མའི་སྤྱིལ་བུ་བྱས
འདུག་པ་དེ་ལ་ཕྱག་ཕེབས། དེ་ནས་བླ་མས་རྒྱལ་བུ་ལ་སྐྲ་བྲུས་གསོལ །
དབུ་སྐྲ་བཞར། རས་བཟང་པོས་ན་བཟའ་བྲེས། ཤིང་ཏིག་ཙེ་མཚར་བའི

f 26

༄༅། །འཆི་བ་ཡང་དག་པ་གནང་། གནས་དེ་ནི་བག་ཤིན་ཏུ
ཕེབས་པ་ཞིག་འདུག །ལྷ་མས་རྒྱལ་བུ་ལ་ཡབ་ཡུམ་འབྲུངས་ཡུལ་སོགས
གང་དང་གང་ཡིན་ཞེས་དྲི་བར་མཛད་པས། ཕྱར་གྱི་ལོ་རྒྱུས་མ་ཆོལ་བར
ཞུས་སོ། །དེར་ལྷ་མ་མཉེས། ཞག་བདུན་སོང་བའི་མཚན་རྟགས་བཟང་ངན
བརྟག་གསུངས། ཡུལ་འདིའི་རྒྱལ་པོ་ཆེན་པོས་སྐབས་འགར་གདན་འདྲེན
བྱེད་ཀྱིན་ཡོད་པས། བདག་ལོ་ཡང་མང་ཙམ་ལོན་པས་ལུས་ཀྱི་མི་ཕེར
བུ་ཆུང་མཚན་དང་ལྡན་པ་ཡིད་དུ་འོང་བ་ཁྱོད་བདག་གིས་བུ་ཚབ་ལ། ཡི་དམ
ཆོས་སྐྱོང་གིས་གནང་བ་ཡིན་འདུག་གསུངས། ལྷ་མའི་མཆོད་གཡོག
མཛད། ནང་རེ་བཞིན་ཤིང་ཏོག་དང་རྩ་དང་མེ་ཤིང་འཐུ་བར་བྱོན། ཀུ་ཤའི
རྩ་ཁྲེས་གཉིས་རེ་འཁུར་བྱོན། དེ་གཅིག་གི་ལྷ་མའི་བཞུགས་གདན་བྱས།
གཅིག་གི་རྒྱལ་བུ་རང་ལ་གཟིམ་མལ་བཟོས་ཏེ་ཉིན་རེ་ཆག་ཆག་དང་ས་གཙང
བར་བྱས་དེ་ནས་ཞག་བདུན་སོང་བའི་ཉིན་མོ་ཉི་མ་རྩེ་ཤར་ལ་རྒྱལ་བུ་ལ་སྐུ
ཁྲུས་གསོལ། ཤིང་ཏོག་ཟ་ཤིང་ཚོགས་མང་པོ་དང་བཅས་དཀོན་མཆོག
ཡི་དམ་ཆོས་སྐྱོང་ལ་གཏང་རག་གི་ཚུལ་དུ་མཆོད་གཏོར་དཔག་ཏུ་མེད་པ
མཛད། ལྷ་མ་ཡབ་སྲས་གཉིས་ཀས་སྨོན་ལམ་ཡང་དག་པར་མཛད། དེ
ནས་ལྷ་མས་དར་གཅིག་ཏིང་ངེ་འཛིན་ལ་བཞུགས། ཏིང་ངེ་འཛིན་དེ་ནས
རྒྱལ་བུ་ལ་བརྟག་པ་མཛད་པས་མངོན་པར་མཁྱེན་པས་མ་འོངས་པའི་ཆེར

༄༅། །མ་ཕྱིན་ཀྱང་ཏ་ལམ་ལས་མ་གསུངས། དེ་ནས་རྒྱལ་
བུ་ལ༔ རྒྱལ་བུ་དོན་ཐམས་ཅད་འགྲུབ་པ་ཕྱིད་འཕགས་པ་སྤྱན་རས་
གཟིགས་ཀྱིས་སྤྲུལ་པར་ཁྲི་ཀོ་མ་མ་མཆིས། སྔོན་ཆད་སྡུག་བསྔལ་དེ་
ལྷ་བུ་ཡབ་ཡུམ་གྱི་བཀའ་མ་བཅག་པ་དཀའ་བ་སྤྱད་པའི་སྙིང་སྟོབས
ཐུགས་བསྐྱེད་དེ་ལྷ་བུ་ངོ་མཚར་ཆེ་སྟེ་མ་འོངས་པ་ན་རྒྱལ་པོ་ཡབ་ཡུམ
གཙུང་པོ་དང་བཅས་ངེད་ཅག་ཡབ་སྲས་ལུས་འདི་མ་པོར་གོང་དུ་མཇལ
བའི་རྟེན་འབྲེལ་བཟང་པོའི་བསྔས་བྱུང་ ཀྱང་། བར་དུ་བདག་ཡབ
སྲས་གཉིས་ལ་བར་གཅོད་ཀྱི་དོ་ཞིག་འདུག་ཏེ། ཡི་དམ་ཆོས་སྐྱོང
ལ་གསོལ་བ་བ་ཏབ་ན་དགའ་རབ་ཡོང་བ་ཀྱང་སྲིད་འདི་ནས་ཐུབ་པའི
བསྟན་པ་སྙིགས་དུས་སུ། རང་ཅག་གཉིས་བསྟན་པའི་བདག་པོར་གྱུར
ཏེ༔ རྒྱལ་པོ་ཡབ་ཡུམ་གཙུང་པོ་དང་བཅས་འཛོམས་ནས་བསྟན་པ
དང་སེམས་ཅན་གྱི་དོན་བྱེད་པར་གྱུར་རོ་ཞེས་ལུང་བསྟན། དེ་ནས་ལྷ
མའི་ཞབས་ཏོག་བསྒྲུབས་ཏེ། ནང་རེ་བཞིན་རྩ་དང་ཤིང་ཏོག་འཐུ་ཡིན
བཞུགས་སོ། །དེ་ནས་ཟླ་བ་གཅིག་སོང་བ་དང་། ལྷ་མས་འདི་སྐད་གསུངས
ཏེ༔ བདག་གི་མ་ལ་གྱི་རྩ་ཆག་པ་དང་། སྙིང་མཐུལ་པ་སོགས་ཡེ་མི་ཡོང།
བུ་ཕྱིད་མགོན་པོ་སྤྱན་རས་གཟིགས་ཀྱི་སྤྲུལ་པ་ཡིན་པ་ལ། །སེམས་ཅན
ཕལ་པ་ལྷ་བུའི་རྩ་ཆག་ཅིང་ཐུལ་བ་འདི་ལྷ་བུ་ཇི་ལྟར་ཡིན། ཕྱིད་ལ་གློས

༄༅། །ཆེན་པོ་ཞིག་འདུག་པ་དེ་བདག་ལ་མ་གསང་བར་ཤོད་
ཅིག་གསུངས་པས། །བདག་བླ་མ་ཇོ་ལ་མི་ཞུ་ན་སུ་ལ་ཞུ། བདག་གི་ནུ་
བོ་སྙིང་དང་འདྲ་བ་ཤི་བས། ནམ་ལ་ཉལ་ཀྱང་གཉིད་ཡོང་བ་མི་འདུག །བླ་
མ་སྐུ་དྲིན་ཆེ་གྲགས་པ་ཡིན་པས། བདག་གི་ནུ་བོའི་རུས་པ་དེ་ལོན་ན་བསམ
པ་གདའ་ལགས་ཞུས་པས། བླ་མས་ཇོ་རྒྱལ་པོའི་གདུང་དྲི་མ་མེད་པ་
འཕགས་པ་སྤྱན་རས་གཟིགས་ཀྱི་སྤྲུལ་པ་འཕགས་པའི་མཛོད་རྩུལ་མ་
ཐུངས་པ་མཚར་སྨུག་ངོ་མཚར་ཅན་འདི་ལྷ་བུ་མཐར་ལ་བཏུགས་པས་རྒྱལ་
པོ་ཡབ་ཡུམ་གཉིས་སྐུ་སྐྱོབས་ཤོག། ནུ་བོའི་རུས་པ་ཡོད་སར་ང་ཅག་
ཕ་བུ་གཉིས་སང་འགྲོ་ཡོ་གསུངས། བུ་དོན་ཐམས་ཅད་འགྲུབ་པ་ཇོད་ཀྱི་
ལམ་སྣ་ཁྲིད་ཤིག་གསུངས། དེའི་སང་ཉིན་བླ་མ་ཡབ་སྲས་གཉིས་ཀྱི་
རིམ་བཞིན་ཇོན་ཏེ། ཞག་གཉིས་སོང་བའི་ཉིན་མོ་ལུང་པ་རི་ཐང་མཚམས་
ཀྱི་ལྡིངས། ནགས་ཚལ་ཤིང་ཏོག་ཡོད་པའི་ས་ཞིག་ཏུ་ཕེབས་དེར་ཞགས་
མཛོད་དེ་བཞུགས་པ་ན། ཁྱི་དང་གཅན་གཟན་རི་དྭགས་རྣམས་ཀྱི་ཉིན་མཚན་
འཁོར་ཡུག་ཏུ་བླ་མ་ཡབ་སྲས་གཉིས་ལ་བསྐོར་བ་བྱེད་བྱ་དང་སྤྲེའུ་རྣམས་
ཀྱིས་ཤིང་ཏོག་ཁྱེར་ཏེ། དེའི་གཙོ་བོ་བརྒྱད་ཀྱིས་ཤིང་ཏོག་ངོ་མཚར་ཅན་མང་
པོ་བླ་མ་ཡབ་སྲས་གཉིས་ཀྱི་སྐུ་མདུན་དུ་ཕྱུངས། ཕྱག་དང་བསྐོར་བ་མང་
པོ་བྱེད། །དེར་རྒྱལ་བུས་ཡབ་རྗེ་བླ་མ་ལ་ཞུས་པ། ཁྱི་དང་རི་དྭགས་གཅན་

༄༅། །གཟན་མང་པོའི་བསྐོར་བ་བྱེད། སྤྲ་དང་སྤྲེའུ་མང་
པོ་ནི་བཀུར་སྟི་མཆོད་པ་གུས་འདུད་འདི་ལྷ་བུ་བྱེད་པ་ངོ་མཚར་ལགས།
དེ་རྣམས་གང་གི་མཐུ་ཡིན་ཞེས་ཞུས་པས། བླ་མས་ཞལ་འཛུམ་པ་
མཛད་དེ། དེད་ཀྱི་བུ་ལེགས་པར་ཉོན་ཅིག །བདག་གི་སངས་རྒྱས་ཀྱི་
ཞིང་མཆོག་བདེ་བ་ཅན་གྱི་མགོན་པོ་འོད་དཔག་མེད་ཀྱི་ཐུགས་ཀ་ནས་
སེམས་ཅན་གྱི་དོན་བྱེད་དུ་འོངས། ཐུ་ཆེད་རི་བོ་པོ་ཏ་ལ་ནས་སེམས་
ཅན་དཔག་ཏུ་མེད་པ་འདྲེན་པའི་དོན་དུ་ཕྱོན་པ་བདག་ཅག་ཡབ་སྲས་དེ་
ལྷ་བུའི་སྨོན་ལམ་གྱི་རྒྱུད་སེམས་ཅན་འདི་རྣམས་ཀྱི་ཤེས་ནས་ཡོངས་
པ་ཡིན། མགོངས་པ་ན་ཤཱཀྱ་ཐུབ་པའི་བསྟན་པའི་དུས་སུ་ཛེ་ཛེ་གདན་
གྱི་བྱང་ཕྱོགས་སུ་སེམས་ཅན་མང་པོའི་དོན་བྱེད། དེའི་དུས་སུ་བྱ་རི་
དྭགས་འདི་རྣམས་བདག་ཅག་གཉིས་ཀྱི་གདུལ་བྱར་གྱུར་པའི་སེམས་
ཅན་མི་རིགས་དང་སྐད་རིགས་མི་གཅིག་པ་མང་པོ་འབྲེལ་ཚད་དོན་
ལྡན་དུ་འགྲོ་བ་ཡིན་གསུངས། རྒྱལ་བུ་ངོ་མཚར་སྐྱེས་ཏེ་ཕྱག་མང་དུ་
བཙལ། །དེ་ནས་ཕར་ཕེབས་པས་གཙུང་གི་གདུང་བཞག་སར་ཕེབས་
སོ༔ ༔དེར་གཡམ་སྒྲོམ་དེ་ནི་མ་ཞིག་པར་འདུག ། དེ་ཁའི་
ཚོགས་སུ་ཤིང་རྟོག་གི་ཤུན་པ་རྩ་མ་ལ་བཟོས་པའི་ཤུལ་དུ་མིས་
བཤད་པ་འདྲ་བཞིག་འདུག །གཞན་ནི་གཙུང་གི་རྫུས་པ་ཙམ་ཡང་མི་

༄༅། །འདུག །དེར་བླ་མ་ཡབ་སྲས་གཉིས་ཀྱིས་ཞག་བདུན་
ཐུག་གཅིག་བཞུགས། ཉིན་རེ་བཞིན་བླ་མས་གཙུང་དོན་ཡོད་ཀྱི་དོན་དུ་བསྔོ་
བ་དང་སྨོན་ལམ་གཏོར་མ་སོགས་མཛད། རྒྱལ་བུས་བླ་མའི་བཞུགས་
གདན་རྩ་སྤུས་མཆོད་པའི་ཤིང་རྟོག་འཕྲུས། རྒྱལ་བུ་ཡིད་སྐྱོ་ནས་ཤིང་
རྟོག་རྩོལ་བ་དང་། བདག་ཅག་གི་ནུ་བོ་གང་ན་ཡོད་ཅེས་སྐད་ཆེན་པོ་གདོང་
ཀྱང་མ་མཇལ་ལོ། །དེར་བླ་མས་ཁྱོད་ནུ་བོ་ལ་གློ་ལས་ཆེན་པོ་འདུག་པ་
བདེན་གསུངས། ཞག་ལྔ་ལོན་པའི་ཉིན་རྒྱལ་བུས་ཤིང་རྟོག་འཕྲུ་བ་དང་
ནུ་བོ་འཚོལ་བར་ཐོན། བླ་མས་གཏོར་མ་གྲུབ་ནས་ཉི་ཟེར་ལ་ཆོས་གོས་
བ་ཀལ་ཏེ་བཞུགས་པ་ན། བླ་མའི་རྩར་ལུང་པ་འདིའི་གཞི་བདག་ཡིན་ཟེར་
གནོད་སྦྱིན་མགོ་བོ་གསུམ་ལག་པ་དྲུག་མདུང་དམ་ཅན་ཞིག་སླེབས་
བྱུང་བས། ཁྱེད་བླ་མ་ཡབ་སྲས་གཉིས་རྒྱལ་པོ་དོན་ཡོད་ལ་ཐུགས་ཁྲལ་
ཆེན་པོ་འདུག་པ་མི་སྨྲོན། ཁོང་དྲང་སྲོང་ཆེན་པོ་ཞིག་གི་ཤི་གསོས་ཀྱི་སྨན་
སྦྱིན་པས་གསོས་ནས་དེ་ནི་ཨ་ཛི་ཆོལ་བར་རི་ཀླུང་ཙུལ་བར་སོང་། ངར་རེས་
ཁྱེད་ཡབ་སྲས་དང་གཙུང་དོན་ཡོད་མཇལ་བའི་སྐལ་བ་མེད། སླར་མཇལ་
བ་ཡོད་དོ་ཞེས་ཞུས། ཁྱེད་ཅི་འདྲ་ཞིག་ཡིན་གསུངས་པས་བདག་གནོད་
སྦྱིན་གྱི་རིགས་ལ་བི་ཀ་ཙེ་ཟེར་བ་ཞིག་ཡིན། མ་འོངས་པར་ཁྱེད་ཡབ་
སྲས་བསྟན་པའི་བདག་པོར་གྱུར་ཞིང་སེམས་ཅན་གྱི་དོན་དཔག་ཏུ་མེད་

༄༅། །ཕ་མཛད་པའི་ཚུལ་སུ་བདག་གིས་སྨྲང་་་མ་ཐེད་པ་
ཡིན་གསུངས། དེར་བླ་མས་ལེགས་སོ་གསུངས་ཏེ་བཀའ་བསྒོ་དམ་
ཚིག་སྒྲོལ་ལོ། །རྒྱལ་བུ་དགོངས་མོ་ཉི་མ་གཞུད་ཁར་འཁོར་རོ། །དེར་བླ་
མས་དེ་རིང་འདིར་གཞི་བདག་ཡིན་ཟེར་བ་གནོད་སྦྱིན་མགོ་བོ་གསུམ་ལག་
པ་དྲུག་པ་མདོག་དམར་མཐུང་དམར་འཁྱེར་བའི་བེ་ཀ་ཙ་ཟེར་བ་འཛིགས་
སུ་རུང་བ་ཞིག་ཡོང་ཏེ། ཁྱེད་བླ་མ་ཡབ་སྲས་གཉིས་རྒྱལ་བུ་དོན་ཡོད་ལ་
ཐུགས་ཁྲལ་ཆེན་པོ་འདུག་མ་སྦྱིན། ཁོང་ལ་དྲང་སྲོང་ཆེན་པོ་ཞིག་གིས་ཤི་
གསོས་ཀྱི་སྨན་སྦྱིན་པས་གསོས་ཏེ། དའི་ཨ་ཛི་ཚོལ་བར་རི་ཀླུང་ཙུལ་བྲར་
ཙོང།
དངེས་ཁྱེད་ཡབ་སྲས་དང་གཙུང་དོན་ཡོད་མཇལ་བའི་སྐལ་བ་མེད། སྐར་
མཇལ་བ་ཡོད་དོ་ཟེར། ཁྱེད་ཙི་འདྲ་ཞིག་ཡིན་དྲིས་པས་གནོད་སྦྱིན་གྱི་
རིགས་བེ་ཀ་ཙ་ཟེར་བ་ཡིན། མ་འོངས་པ་ན་ཁྱེད་ཡབ་སྲས་བསྟན་པའི་
བདག་པོར་འགྱུར་ཞིང་སེམས་ཅན་གྱི་དོན་དཔག་ཏུ་མེད་པ་མཛད་པའི་
ཚུལ་སུ་བདག་གིས་སྨྲང་མ་ཐེད་པ་ཡིན་ཟེར་ཁས་བླངས། བདག་གིས་
དམ་ཚིག་སྒྲོལ་ཞི་བཀའ་བསྒོས་ཏེ་འཕྲིན་ལས་བཅོལ་བ་ཡིན་པས་ངཙག་
ཡབ་སྲས་གཉིས་ཀྱི་དོན་འགྲུབ་པ་འདུག་པས་གློ་ལས་མ་མཛད་ཅིག
གསུངས་པས་རྒྱལ་བུ་མཉེས་ཏེ་བླ་མར་ཕྱག་མཛད་ཐུགས་ལ་བཏགས་ཞེས
ཞུས། དེ་ནས་ཞག་བདུན་སོང་བ་དང་བླ་མ་ཡབ་སྲས་གཉིས་ཕྱིར་ལོག

༄༅། །ཕྱིན་པས། ལམ་ཁར་དུག་སྦྲུལ་དགུ་འདུག་ཏེ་དེ
ནས་གཉིས་ཀྱི་གྲེད་ལ་ན་རེ་སྦྲང་ལམ་བཀག་གོ །དེར་བླ་མའི་དགོངས
པར་ཕྱོག་མར་བླ་མས་འགོམས་ཏེ་ཕྱོག་ན་གཙོད་པ་མི་འབྱུང་དགོངས།
འགོམས་པས་ཞབས་འགྲེད་དེ་སྦྲུལ་གཉིས་ཀྱི་སྐེ་རྡུ་འཁྱིལ་ལོ། །དེར
སྲས་ཀྱིས་ཁྲུག་ནས་འཛིན་པས་བཞེངས་ཐུབ། དུག་སྦྲུལ་གཉིས
པོ་དེ་ཙུང་ཟད་མཆན་ཏེ་ལུས་ལ་ཟུག་ཟྱུང་བས། སྦྲུལ་གཉིས་ཀྱི་བསམ
པ་ལ་སྲས་བུ་ཆུང་འདིས་བླ་མ་འཛིན་པ་མ་གཏོགས་གསོད་ཐག་ཆོད
བསམ་ལོག་ལྷ་སྐྱེས་ཤིང་། ཡིད་ནས་མ་འོངས་པ་ན་བུ་ཆུང་འདིའི
ཞབས་ལ་བཙར་བའི་ཁྲུག་ཁྱེར་སྐྱེས་ཏེ། ཡབ་སྲས་གཉིས་ཀྱི་སེལ
འཇུག་བྱེད་པར་ཤོག་ཅིག །ཅེས་སྨོན་ལམ་ལོག་པར་བཏབ། དུག་སྦྲུལ
ཆུང་བ་བདུན་པོས་ཀྱང་། དེ་བཞིན་དུ་ལོག་ལྷ་སྐྱེས་ནས་རྗེ་ལེབ་དུ
ཕྲིས་སོང་ངོ་། དེར་བླ་མས་ཀྱང་ལོག་ལྷ་དང་སྨོན་ལམ་ལོག་པར
མཁྱེན་ཏེ་སྙིང་རྗེ་ཆེད་མེད་པ་སྐྱེས་ཤིང་། བདེན་ཚིག་བརྗོད་པ་ནི། ཚེ་རབས
དུ་མར་བར་གཅོད་ལོག་ལྷ་དང་། །སྨོན་ལམ་ལོག་པར་བཏབ་པའི་བགེགས
ཀོན༑ ༑བདག་གི་བདེན་པའི་ཚིག་གི་མདོ་བརྗོད་པས། །དེདག་ཐུས
པར་མི་འགྱུར་བདེན་པར་ཤོག །ཡབ་སྲས་དམ་ཚིག་རྡོ་རྗེའི་མདུད་པ
འདི༑ ༑སྐྱེ་བ་དུ་མར་མི་འགྲོལ་འབྲལ་མེད་ཤོག །ཅེས་བདེན་ཚིག

༄༅། །བརྗོད་དོ། །དེ་ནས་བླ་མ་ཡབ་སྲས་རང་གནས་སུ་ཕྱག་
ཕེབས་སྐྱར་བཞིན་རང་གནས་སུ་བཞུགས་སོ། །དེ་ནས་ཉིན་གཅིག་བླ་མས་
བདག་ནི་མཚམས་དང་བསྙེན་པ་འབའ་ཞིག་བྱས་པར་གྱུ་དོག་གི་སྣང་བ་
མི་འདུག་ཀྱང་། །སྒྲུ་ཐོད་ཉེན་རེ་བཞིན་ཆུ་དང་ཤིང་བུ་ལེན། ཤིང་རྡོག་
འཚོལ་བ་སོགས་ལུས་ཀྱིས་པའི་སྒྲུབ་གཡོག་འབའ་ཞིག་གི་གྱུ་དོག །
ཡིད་ནུ་བོའི་སྡུག་བསྔལ་གྱིས་གྱུ་དོག །ངག་ནི་གཞན་ཟླ་བོ་སུ་ཀྱང་མེད་
པས་སྨྲ་བ་བཅད་པར་འགྱུར་པའི་ལུས་ངག་ཡིད་གསུམ་གྱུ་དོག་པས་ངས་
པའི་ཐབས་དེ་རིང་བདག་གི་སྤྱི་ལ་བུ་ནས་ཕར་ཚད་གཅིག་གི་བསིལ་གྲིབ་
ཕྱུར་པ་ཐམས་ཅད་མཐོང་བའི་སྣང་ཞིག་ཏུ་སྨོད་དེ་གསུངས། འབྲས་
ས་ལྷུན་བ་དང་ཤིང་རྟོག་ཀྱང་མང་པོ་བསྣམས་ནས་ཕར་ཚད་གཅིག་ལ་
བཞུགས་སོ། །གུང་སངས་ཞེས་པ་ཀྱང་དེ་ནས་བྱུང་ངོ་། །དེར་བདེ་ལྡན་
དུ་བཞུགས་པའི་བླ་མས་བུ་ལ་མི་རྟག་པའི་ཆོས་གསུངས། དེ་ནས་རྒྱལ་
བུས་བླ་མ་ལ་ཞུས། རང་ཅག་ཡབ་སྲས་ཀྱི་སྤྱིལ་པོའི་ཕ་བོང་ཆེན་པོ་ཕ་
གིའི་འོགས་ན་ལྷའི་གཟུགས་བརྙན་འདྲ་པོ་འདུག་པ་ཕ་ཚོ་ཇི་སྣང་ཡིན་
ཞུས་པས། རིགས་ཀྱི་བུ་ལེགས་པར་ཉོན་ཅིག །སྔོན་དེ་བཞིན་གཤེགས་
པ་འོད་མི་འཁྱུར་བ་ཞེས་བྱ་བའི་དུས་སུ་གནས་འདི་དེ་བཞིན་གཤེགས་
པ་དེའི་བཞུགས་གནས་དང་། དེའི་དུས་སུ་འཕགས་པ་སྤྱན་རས་གཟིགས་

༄༅། །དང་༔ འཇམ་དཔལ་གྱི་སྤྲུལ་པ་བྲམ་ཟེའི་ཁྱེའུ་གཉིས་
བྱུང་སྟེ་སངས་རྒྱས་དེ་ལ་མཆོད་གཉིས་མ་འོངས་པ་ན་གནས་འདིར་འཛོམས་
དུས་ཚོད་
ཏེ་འགྲོ་བའི་དོན་བྱེད་གསུངས་ལུང་བསྟན། དེའི་དུས་བྲག་ཁ་འདི་ལ་རང་བྱོན་
འདི་ལྷ་བུ་ཐེབས་པ་ཡིན། འདིའི་སྟེང་གི་སངས་རྒྱས་ཀྱི་སྐུ་གཟུགས་འདི་དེ་
བཞིན་གཤེགས་པ་ཡེ་ཤེས་འོད་མི་འགྱུར་བ་དང་དབྱེར་མེད་མགོན་པོ་འོད་
དཔག་མེད་ཡིན། དེའི་འོག་ཏུ་གསུམ་འདུག་པ་དེ་གཅིག་སྤྱན་རས་གཟིགས།
དེའི་གཡས་འཇམ་དབྱངས། དེའི་གཡོན་དུ་མཐུ་ཆེན་ཐོབ་པ་བཅས་བྱུང་
སེམས་འོད་དཔག་མེད་ཀྱི་སྤྲུལ་ཡིན། མགོན་པོ་འོད་དཔག་མེད་ནི་ད་ལྟ་
ང་ཡིན། སྤྱན་རས་གཟིགས་ནི་བུ་ཁྱེད་ཡིན། འཇམ་དབྱངས་ནི་ནུ་བོ་
དོན་ཡོད་ཡིན། རང་ཅག་གཉིས་འདིར་འཛོམས་པའི་རྟེན་འབྲེལ་དང་།
ནུ་བོ་ཀུང་མ་འགྱངས་པར་འཕྲད་པའི་རྟེན་འབྲེལ་གྱི་བྱིན་རླབས་ཡིན་
གསུངས། དེར་རྒྱལ་བུ་དགྱེས་ཏེ་ཕྱག་འཚལ་བས་ཁྱེ་རྣམས་ཀུང་འདུས་
ཏེ་བསྐོར་བ་བྱེད། དེར་ཤངས་ཤངས་གཉིས་བབས་བྱུང་སྟེ་གཅིག་གིས་
སེལ་སྨན་ཞིག་དང་། གཅིག་གིས་ནོར་བུ་ཞིག་ཕུལ་ཏེ་མ་འོངས་པ་ན་
ཁྱེད་ཡབ་སྲས་ཀྱིས་རྗེས་སུ་བཟུང་སྟེ་སྦྱིན་བདག་ཏུ་སྐྱེ་བར་ཤོག་ཅིག།
ཅེས་སྨོན་ལམ་ཚིག་གི་གསོལ་བས་བླ་མས་ལེགས་སོ་བརྗོད་ཅིང་ཞལ་གྱི་
བཞེས། དེར་ཁྱེ་སྲིག་པ་ཞིག་བྱུང་སྟེ། བླ་མ་ཨོ་ཟེབ་པ་རྫུན་མ་ཁན་འདི་

༄༅། །ལྷ་བུ་ཡོད་བ་བསམ་འགོག་ལྷ་སྐྱེས་པ་བླ་མས་མཁྱེན་...
ཅིང་སྙིང་རྗེ་སྐྱེས་ཏེ་སྤྲིག་པ་འགོག་ལྷ་མ་བྱེད་གསུངས་པས། མགོ་གྲུག
གྲུག་པ་ལན་གསུམ་བྱས་ཏེ་ཞབས་འབྲིང་དུ་སྐྱེ་པའི་སྨོན་ལམ་བཏབ་...
བོ༔ ༔དེ་ནས་བླ་མ་ཡབ་སྲས་ཀྱིས་འཚུང་དོན་ཡོད་ཀྱི་བུ་མཆོག་ན་མར་...
མཛད་དོ། །དུས་ནམ་ཞིག་ལུང་པའི་མདའ་ན་མི་གྲོང་འདུག་པ་དེར་རྒྱལ་བུ་
འབྲས་ས་ལུ་སོགས་གཟིགས་པ་སྲུ་卐 སྤྲང་ཕྲུག་ཞིག་ཡིན་གསུང་བ་ལས་...
(སྲུ་ཚིན་)
མ་བ་ཤད་དོ། །དེ་ནས་རྗེ་ད་མོ་རྗེ་ད་འཕྲོ་ཁར་ཕྲུ་གུ་ཆོས་འབྲས་བརྟུངས་....
ནས་ཕུལ། །དེའི་ཉིན་ལོག་ཕྱིན་ནས་བླ་མ་དེ་ཁའི་རྒྱུ་མཚན་ཞུས་པས །
བླ་མས་བུ་ཁྱོད་དགའ་རབ་བྱུང་འདུག་ཞབ་ཏུ་མ་བ་ཤད་ན་རྒྱལ་པོས་འཕྲོག་
(བཤད་ཅིག་)
ཉེན་ཡོད་གསུངས། དེ་ནས་ཉིན་གནང་ཆར་སྐབས་འཚམས་སུ་འབྲས་...
སྐྱབ་ཏུ་ཕྱིན་པའི་སྐབས་སུ་སྦྲུ་གུ་ཐམས་ཅད་ཀྱི་ཚོགས་དཔོན་བྱེད། ཁོང་...
རང་ན་མཉམ་ཚོ་དང་འཛིང་ཁ་རྒྱབ་ཀྱང་ཁོང་གིས་ཐམས་ཅད་རྒྱལ་བསྒྱུར།
རྒྱལ་བུས་བདག་འབྲུག་ལོ་པ་ཡིན་པས་གྲགས་པ་འབྲུག་ལས་ཆེ་སྟེང་...
དུ་ཡོད་འདྲ་དེ་བཞིན་ཡིན་གསུངས་ཞལ་ཐད་རེ་ཀྱང་མཛད། ཡུལ་དེའི་...
བླ་མའི་རི་ཁྲོད་དེ་ནས་དཔག་ཚད་ལྷ་འདས་པའི་ཐང་ ཞིག་ན། རྒྱལ་པོའི་
མཁར་གནམ་ལ་སླེག་པ་གཅིག་བྱས། །དེའི་མཐར་མི་གྲོང་འབུམ་ཕྲག་...
གཅིག་གིས་བསྐོར་བ་འདུག །མཐར་ལྕགས་རི་ཆེན་པོ་སྒོ་སྟེང་ཡོད་པ་....

卐 ཐང་ཞིག་ན་བྱིས་པ་མང་པོ་རྩེད་མོ་ལ་འདུག་པ་དེར་ཕྱིན་པས། རྒྱལ་བུ... གཟུགས་བྱེད་མཚར་གྲགས་པས་ཀུན་མཚར་སྐྱེས། གང་ནས་ཡིན... པས་

༄༅། །ཕྱོག་བརྒྱ་ཕྲག་ལྡན་པ་འདུག ། དེ་ལ་ཕྱུག་རྗེར་གྱི་སྐྱུ་ལ...
པ་རྒྱལ་པོ་གོ་ཆ་ཞེས་བྱ་བར་ཕྲས་མོ་མཚར་སྤྱུག་འོད་དང་ལྡན་པ་ཞིག་མ...
གཏོགས་རྒྱལ་བུ་སོགས་གཞན་མེད་པར་འདུག །ཕོ་བྲང་དེ་ནས་དཔག...
ཚད་གཉིས་འདས་པ་ནརྒྱ་མཚོ་ཆེན་པོ་འཁོར་ཡུག་ཏུ་དཔག་ཚད་དྲུག་གི...
བདག་ཉིད་ཅན་ཞིག་ཡོད་པར་འདུག་ཏེ། མཚོ་དེ་ན་དབྱར་ཟླ་ར་བའི་ཚེས་
བཅོ་ལྔ་ལ་གཡུ་འབྲུག་སྔོན་པོ་ནམ་མཁའ་ནས་མར་བབས་ཏེ་མཚོ་ལ...
འབྲུག་སྒྲ་དང་བཅས་འགྲོ །དེར་རྒྱལ་བློན་འབངས་བཅས་ཀྱིས་མཆོད་པ་
ཡང་མཛད། དེའི་མཐུ་ལས་ཆར་ཆུ་དུས་སུ་འབེབས། མི་ནད་ཕྱུགས་ནད་
རྒྱུན་ཆད་པ་བྱུང་བ་ཡོད་པར་གདའ། དུས་ཀྱི་བསྐལ་པ་འགྲིབ་ནས་འབྲུག་
གསོན་མ་དེ་མཚོ་ལ་མ་བབས་པས་ཆར་ཆུ་མ་བྱུང་། མི་ནད་ཕྱུགས་ནད་...
མུ་གེ་སོགས་བྱུང་བས་རྒྱལ་པོས་མོ་ཕྱ་བྱེད་བཅུག་པས་ མོ་མ་དེས།
མཚོ་དེ་ལ་ཀླུའི་རྒྱལ་པོ་དགའ་བོ་དང་། ཉེར་དགའ་དང་། ཀླ་སྐྱུ་ར། ཨ་ནུ་ཧ།
ལག་མངས། ནག་དེ་བ། ཨེ་ལའི་འདབ་མ་སོགས་གནས་འདུག །དེ...
ལ་གཞན་ཐབས་མི་འདུག་མི་འབྲུག་ལོ་པ་དྲུག་གསུམ་བཅོ་བརྒྱད.....
ལོན་པ་ལ་ཀླུ་རྫས་རྟེན་འབྲེལ་ཆས་རྣམས་བསྐྱུར། འཁོར་ལོ་དང......
ཕྱོགས་སྐྱེ་ལ་བཏགས་ཏེ་སྐྱུར་ནས་ཕྱར་དང་འདྲ་བ་འབྱུང་ཞེས་ལུང་བསྟན།
རྒྱལ་པོས་དེ་བཞིན་དུ་མངགས་ཏེ་ཆར་ཆུ་སོགས་ཕྱར་དང་འདྲ་བ་འབྱུང་།

༣༧། ། དེ་ལྟར་ལོ་རེ་བཞིན་དུ་བྱེད་པ་ལ་འབྲུག་ལོ་པ་ལྔ་བཅུ་དྲུག
བཅུ་བདུན་ཙམ་ལོན་པ་རྣམས་ཐེམས་གང་ཐུབ་བྱེད། ཡིན་ཀྱང་མི་འབྲུག
ལོ་པ་རེ་བསྐུར་ནས་རྒྱལ་བློན་རྣམས་རྒྱན་མཆོར་པོ་བཏགས་མཆེད་པ
འབུལ༑ མཚོ་ལ་གསོལ་བ་བཏབ་ན་བསམ་ཚད་ལྷུན་གྱི་གྲུབ་པ་ཡོད་པར
གདའ༑ དེའི་དུས་མཚོ་ལ་ལོ་དུས་ཀྱི་མི་སྐུར་བའི་དུས་ལ་བཅར་ནས།
རྒྱལ་པོས་བློན་པོ་རྣམས་ལ། སྐྱེས་པ་འབྲུག་ལོ་པ་དྲུག་གསུམ་བཅོ
བརྒྱད་སྙིང་ཁར་སླེབ་པ་ཞིག་དགོས་པ་ཚོལ་དུ་བཏང་བས་དུས་ལ་མ་རྙེད།
རྒྱལ་པོ་གོ་ཆ་ལ་ལས་ཀྱི་བློན་པོ་ཏྲི་ཤུ་ཞེས་པ་ཕྲག་དོག་ཞེ་སྡང་གི་མེ
འབར་བ་ཉོན་མོངས་དུག་གསུམ་གྱིས་མྱོས་པ་དེ་བཞིན་གཤེགས་པའི
བཀའ་ལ་ཐེ་ཚོམ་ཟ་བ། མཚོན་ཆའི་རིགས་རྒྱུན་དུ་འཆང་ཞིང་དགའ་བ
ཞིག་ཡོད། དེས་སྔར་གྱི་མི་གསོན་མ་མང་པོ་མཚོ་ལ་སྐུར་བའི་འཁུར
ལེན་བྱེད་ཅིང་། དེའི་སློན་ལམ་མ་ལོག་པའི་མཐུས། རྒྱལ་བུ་དོན་ཐམས
ཅད་འགྲུབ་པ་འབྲུག་ལོ་པ་བཅོ་བརྒྱད་མཆོ་པེབས་པ་བླ་མ་ལེགས་པའི
བློ་གྲོས་ཀྱི་སློབ་བུར་ཡོད་པ། ཐུ་གུ་གཞན་ཚོས་སྐད་ཆ་རེམ་པར་མཆེད་དེ
ཐོས་པས་ཡིད་དགའ་སྟེ། རྒྱལ་པོ་ལ་ལན་ཞུས་པས། དེ་བྱེད་རང་གི
ང་ལྟ་རང་ཁྱུག་ཤོག་གསུངས། དེར་བློན་པོ་ཏྲི་ཤུས་བླ་མའི་སློབ་བུའི་རྩར
ཕྱིན༑ བླ་མས་པོ་ཉ་བློན་པོ་མ་སླེབ་གོང་དུ་མངོན་པར་མཁྱེན་པས་ཤེས

༄༅། །ཏེ། རིགས་ཀྱི་བུང་ཅག་གཉིས་ལ་རྒྱལ་པོའི་……
འཇིགས་པས་ཁྱོད་འཕྲོག་ཏུ་ཡོང་བ་འདུག་པས། ད་ནི་བུ་ཁྱོད་རྩའི་……
གསེབ་ཏུ་གབ་ཅིག་གསུངས། སྤྱིལ་བུའི་སྦུག་ན་ཀུ་ཤ་མང་པོ་ཡོད་པའི་
གསེབ་ཏུ་སྦས། དེའི་སྟེང་དུ་ཛ་ཏིག་མ་ཁ་སྦུག་ཏེ་བཞག །བདག་གི་ལབ་
མ་ཐུས་བར་དུ་མ་འཐོན་ཅིག །བུ་ཁྱོད་ཀྱི་སྐད་ཐོས་ན་ཁྱོད་འཇེར་མཆོར་
སྐྱུར་ཉེན་ཡོད་དོ་གསུངས། དེར་བློན་པོ་སློབ་པ་དང་། བླ་མས་མགྱོགས་
པར་སྤྱིལ་བུའི་སྒོ་འགག་ཏུ་ཕྱིན། དེར་ཏྲི་ཤུས་བླ་མ་ཁྱེད་ལ་བུ་ཞིག་ཡོད་…
འདུག་པས། རྒྱལ་པོས་འགུག་པར་བདག་མངགས་བྱུང་བས་གར་ཡོད་…
ཤོད་ཟེར། བདག་ལ་སྤྲུབ་ཟླ་མེད་སྤྲུབ་པ་ཅེད་མཁན་དགེ་སློང་མི་གཅིག…
བུལ་བུ་ཚིག་ལ་ཡོད། ཞེས་གསུངས་པས། མི་བཤོད་ན་བླ་མ་རང་བདེ་…
མོ་མི་ཡོང་ཟེར། དེར་བླ་མས། བདག་ལ་བཤད་རྒྱུ་ནི་མེད། བདག་སྤྲུབ་པ་
མི་གཅིག་ཡིན་ཆགས་པ་ཞེན་པ་མེད་པས་གསོད་ན་ཡང་གསོད་ཟེར་བླ་……
མས་སྨུར་ཐུག་བཙོང་ངོ། །དེར་ཕོ་སྤྱིལ་བུའི་ཕུག་ཏུ་འཚང་ནས་གཡུལ་…
བས་མ་རྙེད་དེར་བློན་པོ་ཏྲི་ཤུས་བླ་མ་གསོད་པ་ཡིན་ཟེར་གྲི་ཛམ་ཛམ……
བྱས་པས། རྒྱལ་བུས་རྩའི་གསེབ་ནས་གཟིགས་པ་དང་བདག་གི་བླ་
མ་སྐུ་དྲིན་ཅན་འདི་བདག་གིས་མ་ཕྱིན་ན་གསོད་པར་འདུག་པས་མི་
རུང་དགོངས་ཏེ། རྒྱལ་བུས་རྩའི་གསེབ་ནས་ཕྱིན་ཏེ། བདག་གི་དྲིན་ཅན་

༄༅། །ཀྱེ་བླ་མ་འདི་ལ་དེ་འདྲ་མི་མཛད་པ་ཞུ་གསུངས། བུ་
ཆུང་འདི་ཡིན་ཟེར་ལ་གནས་འཕྲེད། བླ་མས་འཛུམ་ཀྲང་མ་ཐུབ། བློན་
པོ་ཏྲི་ཤུས་བླ་མ་ལ་ལོག་ལྟ་སྐྱེས་ཏེ། དགེ་སློང་ཁྲམ་སྤྱོལ་འདྲི་འདྲ་
ཡོད་པ་ཨང་། ཁོ་ལ་བུད་སྨེད་ན་ཨ་ཕ་ཨ་མ་ཡུལ་ཕྱོགས་གང་ཡང་བསྒོད
རྒྱུ་མེད་པའི་ཕྲུག་གུ་ཡོད་པ་ཨེ་སྲིད་ཟེར་ཡིད་ལ་བབས་མ་ཞེང་ཁ་ལ་ཡང་
སྨོན་ཏེ་བླ་མར་བྲང་འཛོག་གསུམ་རྒྱབ་ནས་གན་རྒྱལ་དུ་སྐྱོལ་ནས་ཁོང་
རྣམས་ཤོར་སོང་ངོ་། །བླ་མས་སྨོན་ལམ་དགོངས་ཞིགས་མ་ཆག་པར་མཛད།
དཀོན་མཆོག་ལ་གསོལ་བ་བཏབ་ཏེ་འདི་སྐད་བརྗོད་དོ། ༈ །བླ་མ་ཡི་
དམ་ཆོས་སྐྱོང་རྣམས། །བདག་ལ་དགོངས་ཞིང་ཐུགས་རྗེས་སྐྱོབས་དུ་
གསོལ། །དཀོན་མཆོག་ཐུགས་རྗེའི་སྤྲུལ་པའི་སྲས་མཆོག་འདི། །ལྷ་དང་
བླ་མས་དངོས་གྲུབ་སྐུལ་བ་ཡི། །བར་ཆད་བདུད་ཀྱི་སྤྲུལ་པས་ཁྲིད་དེ་སོང་།
བདག་གི་བུ་ལ་སྡུག་བསྔལ་མ་མྱོང་ཅིག །བདག་ཅག་སྐྱེ་བ་མང་པོའི་ཡབ་
སྲས་ཡིན། །ད་དུང་མྱུར་དུ་མཛལ་བའི་སྨོན་ལམ་འདེབས། །ཅེས་བདེན་
ཚིག་བརྗོད་དོ། །དེ་ནས་རྒྱལ་པོ་གོ་ཆའི་བྲང་དུ་ཕྱིན་པས། རྒྱལ་པོས་བུ་
ཆུང་མཚར་ཞེས་རྒྱལ་པོ་མཉེས། ཞག་བདུན་རྒྱལ་པོའི་ཕོ་བྲང་དུ་བཞུགས་
པ་ན་རྒྱལ་པོའི་སྲས་མོ་ལྷ་གཅིག་འོད་ལྡན་མ་མཚར་སྡུག་འོད་དང་ལྡན་པ་
ཞིག་ཡོད་པ་དེ། རྒྱལ་བུ་ལ་སེམས་ཤོར་སྟེ། རྒྱལ་བུ་དང་ཁོང་གཉིས་

༄༅། །དགའ་མཐུན་བྱུང་སྐྱེ་འབྲལ་མི་ཡོད་པ་འདུག་པ་ལྟར་
གྱུར་ཏོ། །རྒྱ་མཚོའི་དུས་རབས་ལ་ཁད་ཉེར་སོང་དེ་ནས་རྒྱལ་པོས་བདག་གི
བུ་མོ་འདི་དང་བུ་ཆུང་འདི་གཉིས་འབྲལ་མི་ཡོད་པ་འདུག་པས། བློན་པོ་
རྣམས་ཀྱིས་སྐྱེས་པ་འབྲུག་ལོ་པ་བཅོ་བརྒྱད་པ་གཞན་ཆོལ་ཤོག་གསུངས།
བློན་པོ་གཞན་རྣམས་ཀྱི་སྨྲ་མ་ནུས། བློན་པོ་ཊྲི་ཤུས། རྒྱལ་པོས་སྨྲ་བ་ལན་
གཅིག་ཡིན་པ་ལ། དེ་ལས་མང་ན་རྒྱལ་ཁྲིམས་ཆལ་འགྲོ་ཟེར། ཆབ་འབངས་
ཀྱིས་ཀྱང་བསྐུར་བ་ཡོང་ཟེར་མུར་ཐུག་བཙོངས་སོ། །བླ་མ་དེ་ཡང་ཚད་ལྡན་
མི་འདུག །ཁོང་ལ་བུ་འདི་ཧྲ་བུ་འདུག་པ་ལ་བུད་མེད་མེད་པར་བུ་ཡོང་བ་ག་
ལ་སྲིད། བླ་མ་དེ་ཆོས་མི་ན་ཁྲམ་པ་ཞིག་འདུག་ཟེར། དེར་རྒྱལ་བུའི་
ཐུགས་ལ་ལྷ་གཅིག་འོད་ལྡན་མ་འདི་མི་ཡོད་འདུག་ཀྱང་བདག་གི་མ་ཕྱིན་
ན་ཚབ་ལ་སྐྱེས་པ་ཞན་འགྲོ་དགོས་སྙིང་རྗེ་དགོངས་ནས། བདག་པས་
གཞན་གཅེས་ཀྱི་བྱམས་པའི་སེམས་ཀྱིས་རྒྱལ་བུ་བློན་པོ་རྣམས་ལ་
གྲོས་སྟོན་ཏེ། སྲས་མོ་ལྷ་གཅིག་འདིས་བདག་ལ་འཆང་ནས་མི་གཏོང་
པ་འདུག །ནོར་བུ་འདོན་པའི་གླུའི་ནང་དུ་ཁྱེད་རང་བློན་པོ་གྲུ་དང་བཅས་
ང་ཚག་གཉིས་སྔོན་ནས་འགྲོ་ཡོ། །དེར་སྲས་མོ་གཉིད་དུ་སོང་བ་དང་
ཁྱེད་རང་ཚོས་ལྷ་གཅིག་དེ་ཟུངས་ལ་ས་མ་གཏོང་། བདག་གི་རིགས་
དྲུག་སེམས་ཅན་གྱི་དོན་འབའ་ཞིག་བསྒྲུབ། སོམ་ཉི་མེད་པར་རྒྱ་མཚོར

༄༅། །འགྲོ་ཡི་གསུངས་པས། བློན་འབངས་ཀུན་ཏ་ལས་ངོ་...
མཚར་དུ་གྱུར་ཏོ། །དེའི་དུས་བློན་པོ་ལྷ་བས་བྱིན་དང་ཀ་རྟེ་ཀ་གཉིས་ལཀྵ
ཏེ༔ ཕྱག་བཙལ་མཆི་མ་འཁྲུག་ཅིང་བདག་གཉིས་ཀྱང་ཕྱིད་ཀྱི་རྗེས་སུ་...
བཟུངས་ཟེར་རོ། །དེ་ནས་རྒྱལ་བུ་ལྷ་གཅིག་བློན་པོ་ཀྱང་འཁོར་དང་བཅས་...
པ་གླུའི་ནང་དུ་བཞུགས་ཙོན་པ་ན། སྲས་མོ་ལྷ་གཅིག་གིས་རྒྱལ་བུར་ཉིན་...
མཚན་མེད་པར་འཆང་ནས་གཏོང་མ་ཉན། དེ་ནས་སྐབས་ཞིག་སྲས་མོའི་
ལག་པ་ལྗོད་པ་ཞིག་བྱུང་བས། བློན་པོ་རྣམས་ལ་ཕྱག་གི་བརྡ་མཛད།
རྒྱལ་བུས་སྙིང་རྗེའི་སེམས་ཀྱིས་རྒྱ་མཚོ་ལ་འཚོངས་སོ། །དེའི་ཚོ་ནམ་......
མཁའ་ནས་སྒྲ་འོད། འཇའ་གུར། མེ་ཏོག་གི་ཆར་བབས་ས་གཡོས། བར་
སྣང་ནས་འབྲུག་དང་གློག་ལ་སོགས་པ་བྱུང་བར་སྲས་མོ་བློན་པོ་རྣམས་...
ཀྱིས་བཟུངས་ནས་པོ་བྲང་དུ་ལོག་གོ །རྒྱལ་པོ་ཆོས་བློན་གཉིས་དང་བཅས་
འཁྱོད་པ་སྐྱེས་ཏེ་བཤགས་པ་བྱེད། སྲས་མོ་ལྷ་གཅིག་མ་དང་བཅས་ཏྱི་...
ངན་གྱིས་ངོན་ནོ། །དེའི་དུས་སུ་རྒྱ་མཚོ་ཆེན་པོ་དེའི་དཀྱིལ་ན་ཀླུའི་རྒྱལ་པོ་...
ཉེར་དགའ་དང་འཛིན་པ་ལག་མངས་སོགས་ཀྱི་དབུས་ཀླུ་ཕོ་མོ་བས་མ་གྱི་...
མི་ཁྱབ་པ་ཉེར་དགའི་པོ་བྲང་དུ་འཛོམས་པ། དེར་རྒྱལ་བུ་ཟེལ་པ་ཁྲིམ་མེ་...
ཁོང་ཚོའི་རྩར་ཐེབས་པ་དང་། ཁོང་རྣམས་ཀྱིས་རྒྱལ་བུ་མཚར་བས་......
བཞེངས་པ་བྱས་བསྐོན་བཀུར་ཕུན་སུམ་ཚོགས་པ་བྲངས་སོ། །སྔར་......

༄༅། །ཡིན་ན་མི་རེ་སྔེར་བར་ལུས་སེམས་བྲལ་ནས་ཡོངས། ངུ་
སྒྲ་ཆེན་པོས་ཀླུ་ཡུལ་དུ་ཁྲག་གི་ཆར་འབབ། ད་རེས་ཆོས་རྒྱལ་ཁྱེད་ཕེབས་
པས་རོལ་མོའི་སྒྲ་དང་། མེ་ཏོག་དང་ཤིང་ཐོག །རྫི་ཏི་ཕལ་ཀླུ་སྨན་བཟང་
པོ་དང་བཅས་པའི་ཆར་བབས། དེད་ཀྱི་ལུང་པ་ཀུང་བཙུད་དང་ལྡན་པ་
པ་བྱུང་། དེའི་མཐུས་སེམས་ཅན་རྣམས་གདུག་རྩུབ་ཞི་སྡེ་དེ་ཀླུ་རྣམས་
ཚེ་རིང་། ལོངས་སྤྱོད་རྒྱས། ཤི་ནས་ཀྱང་ལྷ་དང་མིའི་ལུས་སུ་སྐྱེ་བ་
འདུག་ཟེར་དགའ་གྲགས་སོ། །དེའི་དུས་སུ་སྐབས་ཞིག་ཀླུ་རྣམས་ཀྱིས་
རྒྱལ་བུ་ལ་ཞུས་པ། འདི་ནས་ཡར་རང་ཡུལ་དུ་འཇོན་ནམ། ངེད་ཀླུའི་
འགྲོ་མགོན་ལ་བཞུགས་ཞེས་ཞུས་པས། རྒྱལ་བུས་བདག་སེམས་ཅན་
གྱི་དོན་བྱེད་པ་ལ་གར་སྡོད་ཀྱང་ཁྱད་པར་མེད། འོན་ཀྱང་བདག་གི་བླ་མ་
མགོན་པོ་འོད་དཔག་མེད་ཀྱི་སྤྲུལ་པ་ཁྱད་པར་དུ་འཕགས་པ་ཞིག་ཡོད་པ་
དེ་ཕྱུགས་ཁྲལ་ལ་གཏད་ཡོད་པས། བདག་ལན་ཅིག་འགྲོ་དགོས་ཡོད་པས།
ཁྱེད་རྣམས་རྟུང་དང་ཕྲག་དོག་མ་བྱེད་པར་ཕྱོངས་ཤིག་ཁྲོལ་བར་མཛོད་དུ་
ཀ་སོལ་
གསུངས། སྔར་གྱི་ལོ་རྒྱུས་རྣམས་ཀྱང་མ་འཆོལ་བར་གསུངས་སོ། །
ཀླུའི་རྒྱལ་པོ་དགའ་བོ་ཨེ་ལ་དང་། ཉེར་དགའ་བོས་ཕྱོགས་བྲངས་ཀླུ་བྱེའུ་དྲུག་
གི་ཚོགས་རྣམས་ཡིད་རང་ངོ་། །ངོ་མཚར་སྐྱེས་ཏེ་ཕྱག་དང་མཆོད་པ་དཔག་
མེད་ཞུས། ཀླུ་ཡུལ་དུ་མིའི་ཞག་ནས་ཟླ་བ་གསུམ་བཞུགས་པའི་

༄༅། །རིང་ཆོས་གསུངས། དེ་ནས་ཀླུ་རྣམས་ཀྱིས་ཞུས་པ།
ཁྱེད་ཀྱི་སྐུ་དྲིན་ལ་བདག་ཅག །ལྷ་ཀླུ་རྣམས་གཟུགས་དང་དབང་པོ་ཉམས་
པ་རྣམས་གསོས་ཤིང་ལོངས་སྤྱོད་རྒྱས་བདེ་བ་ཕུན་སུམ་ཚོགས་པ་བྱུང་ད་
ནི་ཁྱེད་ཀྱི་ཐུགས་རྗེ་ལས་ཕྱིས་སུ་མཚོ་འདི་ལ་མི་གཞན་མ་སྐྱུར་མི་དགོས་
པ་བྱེད་ལགས་ཞུས། དེ་ནས་རྒྱལ་པོ་ལ་ཀླུའི་རྒྱལ་པོ་ཉི་ར་དགའ་དང་ཚེ་
ལ་གཉིས་ཀྱིས་ཡིད་བཞིན་གྱི་ནོར་བུ་བསམ་འཕེལ་དང་པའི་སྒོང་ཙམ་རེས་
ཕོག་དྲངས་ནོར་བུ་དཔག་མེད་ཕུལ། ཀླུ་དྲུང་སྐྱོང་ས་དང་འཛིན་པ་ལག་
མངས་གཉིས་ཀྱིས་ཀྱང་ནོར་བུ་བཻ་ཌཱུརྱའི་རིགས་མང་པོ་དང་བཅས་ཀླུ་དམངས་
རྣམས་ཀྱིས་ཀྱང་ནོར་བུ་སྣ་རེ་ཕུལ། ཐམས་ཅད་ཀྱིས་སྨོན་ལམ་བཏབ །
རྒྱལ་བུས་རྗེས་སུ་འཛིན་པ་ཞལ་གྱིས་བཞེས། དེ་ནས་ཀླུ་རྣམས་ཀྱིས་གདན་
འདྲེན་གྱི་ཚུལ་བྱས། རྒྱལ་བུས་སྤྱན་རྩུམ་སྟེ་བདག་གི་བླ་མའི་རྩར་འགྱོར་
པར་ཤོག་ཅིག །ཅེས་སྨོན་ལམ་བཏབ་པས། དེ་མ་ཐག་ཏུ་བླ་མའི་སྤྱིལ་བུའི་
འགག་ཏུ་ཕྱུག་ཕེབས། བདག་གི་བླ་མ་འདི་འདྲ་ཡོང་བ་ཨང་། བདག་སླེབས་
ཡོད་ཐུགས་ཁྲལ་མ་མཛད་པ་ཞུ་ཞུས་པས། བདག་གི་བུ་དེ་འདྲ་མཚོ་ལ་
སྐྱུར་ནས་མེད་པས་ཤི་ཚར་ནས་ལོག་པའི་ཁ་ལེ་མི་འདུག །ཁྱེད་ཀྱི་བདག་
ལ་སྙིང་ཆེམས་སེམས་དཀྲུག་རྒྱུ་ཨེ་ཡིན་གསུངས་བླ་མ་བརྒྱལ་ལོ། །དེར་
ཙན་དན་གྱི་བུམ་ཆུ་གཏོར་བས་སོས། ཤ་སྐམ་གྱི་ཐུག་པ་སྣུམ་གྱི་བཀུ་མཉེས

༄༅། །སོགས་མཛད། སྨན་སྐྱུག་བསལ་ཏེ་བླ་མའི་འགྲུལ་
ལ་འབྱུང་ནས། བླ་མ་ལ་བུ་དོན་འགྲུབ་ཡིན་གསུངས་པས། བླ་མ་མཉེས་
གྲགས་ཤི་གསོན་འཕྲད་པ་ལྟར་གྱུར་ཏོ། །དེར་བླ་མས་རྒྱལ་བུ་ལ་ཇི་ལྟར་
གྱུར་དྲི་བ་མཛད་པས། རྒྱལ་བུས་ཁོང་རང་གི་ལོ་རྒྱུས་རྣམས་ཞིབ་པར་
ཞུས། ནོར་བུ་བསམ་འཕེལ་གྱི་དབུས་མཐུ་བ་གང་བསྣམས་ཡོད་པ་ཀྱང་
བླ་མར་ཕུལ་བས་བླ་མ་མཉེས་གྲགས། བདག་གི་བུ་འདི་འདྲ་སྐྱེལ་བའི་རྒྱལ་
པོ་འཇིག་རྟེན་ན་དཀོན། རིགས་དྲུག་སེམས་ཅན་ཀུན་ལ་སྐྱུ་དྲིན་ཆེ་གསུངས།
བླ་མ་ཡབ་སྲས་གཉིས་པོ་བཞུགས་ན་གདན་གཅིག །བཞེས་ན་སྟོད་གཅིག་
གི་འབྲལ་མི་ཕོད་པ་ལྟར་གྱུར་ཏོ། །དེར་རྒྱལ་པོ་གོ་ཆས། རང་གི་བླ་མའི་
སྲས་བུ་ཆུང་མཆོལ་སྐྱུར་བས་ཕྱུར་བསལ་ལོ་ལེགས། ནད་རིམས་ཀྱི་རྒྱུན་
ཆད། ཆར་ཆུ་དུས་སུ་ཕེབས། ལོངས་སྤྱོད་བདེ་སྐྱིད་ཕུན་སུམ་ཚོགས་
པ་བྱུང་བས་བླ་མ་གདན་འདྲེན་པར་བཏང་། ཞབས་གཏོགས་ཕུན་སུམ་
ཚོགས་པ་ཞུས་པ་དྲག་ཟེར། བློན་པོ་ཐམས་ཅད་དེ་དགའ་ཞེས་ཁ་
མཐུན། བློན་པོ་དྲི་ཤུས་བླ་མ་རང་རེའི་ཁོངས་ཡིན་པ་ལ་དཔོན་གྱིས་
འབངས་ལ་དྲིན་བཟློའི་བཀུར་སྟི་ག་ལ་ནོས་ཟེར་མ་དགའ་འོ། །དེར་བློན་པོ་
གཞན་རྣམས་ཁ་མཐུན་པས། རྒྱལ་པོས་བློན་པོའི་ཁྲིད་ནས་བླ་མ་ལ་
དད་མོས་ཆེ་བ་ཞིག་བླ་མ་གདན་འདྲེན་ལ་སོང་ཞིག་ཅེས་བཀའ་གནང་ངོ་། །

༄༅། །དེར་བློན་པོ་ཆོས་དཔལ་འབར་ཞེས་བྱ་བའི་ཆོས་བློན་དེས་
བདག་གི་འགྲོ་གསུངས་ནས། འབངས་འཁོར་འཚུ་ཕྲུག་གཅིག་ཁྲིད་དེ་སོང་
ངོ་༔ ༔དེར་བླ་མའི་སྒོ་དྲུང་དུ་སླེབ་པ་དང་། བླ་མ་རིན་པོ་ཆེ་ལགས། ཁྱེད་···
ཀྱི་ཡུས་རྒྱལ་བུ་དོན་ཐམས་ཅད་འགྲུབ་པ་མཆོལ་སྤྱུར་བས། ཡུལ་ཁམས་···
ཐམས་ཅད་བདེ་སྐྱིད་ཕུན་སུམ་ཚོགས་པ་བྱུང་། དགེ་སྐུ་དྲིན་བསབ་ཕྱིར་དུ་
རྒྱལ་པོས་བླ་མ་ལ་མཆོད་བཀུར་སྒྲི་དཔག་ཏུ་མེད་པ་ཞུ་བས། བདག་གདན་···
འདྲེན་ལ་བཏང་བྱུང་བས་བྱོན་ཞིག་ཞུས། འོན་ཁྱེད་རྣམས་འདིའི་ཤམ་མ་···
གིར་བཞུགས་ཤིག །བདག་གི་ཆོས་གོས་སོགས་བརྗེས་ཏེ་སླེབ་ཡོང་······
གསུངས། དེ་ནས་བུ་འདི་འཇིག་པ་སེམས་ཀྱི་མི་ཕོད་འདུག །ཁྲིད་ནའི་···
རྒྱལ་པོས་གཟིགས་ཏེ་ད་དུང་འཕྲོག་ཉེན་ཡོད་དགོངས་ཙན། རྒྱལ་བུས་····
བདག་གི་སྤྲང་རྫུས་བཏབ། གདོང་ལ་རས་ཀྱི་འབབ་སྒྱོན་ཏེ་ཕྱག་ཕྱིར་ཕྱིན་
ཆོག་གསུངས་འོན་སྒྲིབ་བྱེད་དེ་གས་ཡོང་···འགྲོ་གསུངས་ནས་རྒྱལ་བུར་···
སྤྲང་རྫས་དང་རས་ཀྱི་འབབ་གཡོགས། བླ་མའི་ན་བཟའ་བེར་དང་དབང་···
ཆས་རྣམས་རྒྱལ་བུས་རྒྱབ་ཏུ་ཁུར་ནས་བྱོན། བློན་པོས་བླ་མར་ཆིབས་པ་···
གནང་ཞུ་ཞུས་པས། བདག་གིས་རྐང་བཞིའི་བཞོན་པ་སྤྲངས་ནས་མེད་······
གསུངས། ཞབས་ཐང་དུ་རྒྱལ་བུས་ཕྱག་ནས་འཛུས་ཏེ་བྱོན་ནོ། །དེར་བློན་
པོས་བླ་མའི་ཉེ་གནས་འདི་ཡུལ་གནས་ཡིན། འདིའི་གདོང་སྐྱོན་མི་ནུས་··· 卐

卐 པ་ཇི་ལྟར་ཡིན་ཞུས་པས། དེར་བླ་མས་བདག་གི་ཉེ་གནས་འདི་སྔར་པོ་····· དབུལ་པོ་ཞིག་གི་སྤྱིན་བྱུང་།
གདོང་སྐྱོན་མི་ནུས་པ་ནི་དབུལ་པོ་ཕ་བུ་བྱུང་ ཐང་མང་པོ་འགྲིམ་ནས་ཡོང་བའི་ལམ་ཁར་དུག་སྦྲང་གི་གདོང་
པར་གནོད་ སྨྱོལ་བས་དེ་ལ་གཉན་རྒྱབ་པས་དེ་མ་གསོས་བར་དུ་གདོང་སྐྱོན་མི་····· ནུས།

༄། །ཉི་ལྟག་རྒྱ་གར་མི་ཐུབ་པ་ཡིན་གསུངས། དེ་ནས་རྒྱལ་པོ
གོ་ཆའི་པོ་བྲང་དུ་ཕྱག་ཕེབས། དེར་བླ་མ་ལ་གདན་འབོལ་གབ་རྫེ་གསུམ
བརྩེགས་ཞིག་གཏིང་བའི་སྟེང་དུ་གདན་དྲངས། ཉེས་གནས་རྒྱལ་བུལ·····
ཡང་གདན་རྒྱང་ཞིག་གཏིངས། དེར་བླ་མ་ཡབ་སྲས་ཀྱིས་ཤིང་ཏོག་གི·····
ཕྱག་རྟེན་རེ་ཡང་ཕུལ། དེར་བླ་མ་ལ་རྒྱལ་པོས་ཞག་བདུན་བཞུགས་དགོས
ཞེས་ཞུས་ཏེ་ཞལ་གྱི་བཞེས་བ་ཀུར་སྐྱེ་ཞབས་ཏོག་འབུལ་བ་ཕུན་སུམ·····
ཚོགས་པ་ཞུས། དེར་བླ་མ་ལ་རྒྱལ་པོས་ཞུས་པ། བླ་མ་དམ་པའི་སྲས
གཅིག་པོ་དེ་མཚོ་ལ་གདན་འདྲེན་ཞུ་དགོས་པ་ཡོང་ཏེ། བླ་མ་ཐུགས་བྲལ་ལ
གཏད་འདུག་པ་བཟོད་པར་གསོལ། སྲས་པོ་མཚོ་ནང་དུ་ཐོན་པ་ནས།
སེམས་ཅན་ཐམས་ཅད་བདེ་སྐྱིད་ཕུན་སུམ་ཚོགས་པ་ཀུང་འབྱུང་བས་དེའི
བཀའ་དྲིན་གསབ་ཕྱིར་གདན་དྲངས་པ་ཡིན་ཞུས་པས། བླ་མས་ལེགས···
སོ་རྒྱལ་པོ་བློན་པོ་དང་བཅས་པ་ཉེན་ཅིག་གསུངས་ནས། རྒྱལ་བུའི་སྐོར
གྱི་ལོ་རྒྱུས་བརྗོད་པས་ཀུན་ངོ་མཚར་ཞིང་བླ་མ་ལ་ཕྱག་བཙལ་ལོ། །དེ····
ནས་ཞག་བཞི་སོང་སོང་ཐུག་པ་རྒྱལ་བུ་ཡིན་པ་ངོམ་ཤེས། ཞག་ལྔ་སོང
བའི་ཉིན་པོ་བྲང་གི་རྩེ་ན་བླ་མ་དང་རྒྱལ་པོ་བློན་པོ་དང་བཅས་ཕྱོགས་བསྐོར
མཇོད་ཀྱི་ཡོད་པ་དེར་སྲས་མོ་ལྷ་གཅིག་འོད་ལྡན་མ་དེ་ཕྱག་ལ་བསེ་རུའི
རྭ་དང་། གླང་པོ་ཆེའི་མཆེ་བ། རི་དྭགས་ཨེ་ཙ་ཡའི་པགས་པ་བཅས·····

༄༅། །ཕྱིར་ཏེ་བླ་མ་ལ་ཕྱུལ་ཕྱག་བཙལ་ཕྱིན་རླབས་ཞུས། རྒྱལ་
བུ་དོན་ཐམས་ཅད་འགྲུབ་པ་མཚོན་དང་དུག་ཤིགས་པ་བླ་མས་ཐུགས་རྗེས་
བཟུང་ཞེས་བ་ཤུམ་མོ། །དེར་བླ་མ་ཡང་སྙིང་རྗེ་དཔག་ཏུ་མེད་པ་སྐྱེས།
ལྷ་བླ་མའི་ཐུགས་རྗེས་མི་སྐྱོན། རྒྱལ་བུ་དང་ཕྱིད་རང་གཉིས་སྔོན་གྱི་སྐལ་
པ་ཡོད་པས་མཇལ་ཡོང་གསུངས་པའི་མོད་ལ། རླུང་ཆེན་པོ་ཞིག་ལང་
ཕྱུང་བ་དང་བླ་མའི་དབུ་ཞྭ་ཕྱིར་བས་རྒྱལ་བུས་དེ་ལ་འཇུར་བཟུངས་པས་བད་
ཀྱི་སྣང་སྣ་ཞིག་ལ་དབུ་བརྡབས་འབབ་གི་སྒྲོ་ཁ་ཆད་ནས་ཞལ་མཐོང་།
དེར་བློན་པོ་རྣམས་ཀྱི་རྒྱལ་བུ་ཕྱག་ཕེབས་ཞེས་ཕྱག་བཙལ་བས། དེར་
རྒྱལ་པོ་ཡབ་དང་སྲས་མོ་ལྷ་ཅིག་བཅས་པས་ཀྱང་རྒྱལ་བུ་ངོ་ཤེས། དེར་
སྲས་མོས་རྒྱལ་བུ་ལ་འཆངས། ཕོ་རྣམ་གཉིས་གཅིག་ལ་གཅིག་འཆང་
ཤིག་སོན་འཕྲད་པ་འདི་འདྲ་ཡོང་བ་ཨང་གསུངས། དེར་རྒྱལ་པོ་གོ་ཆ་
བློན་འབངས་དང་བཅས་པ་ངོ་མཚར་ཆེ་གྲགས། ཐམས་ཅད་ཀྱིས་ཞོར་བུ་
སྔ་རེས་ཐོག་དྲངས་འབུལ་བ་ཇམས་ཆེ་བཕུལ། འདི་འདྲ་ཡོང་བ་ཅི་ཡིན་
ཟེར་བླ་མ་ལ་ཞུས་པས། རྒྱལ་པོ་སྔ་ལ་དེ་བའི་སྲས་རྒྱུད་མཐར་བཙུག་
ལུགས་དང་བླ་ཕུལ་དུ་འཛིན་ལུགས་སོགས་ཞིབ་པར་གསུངས་པས་ཀུན་
ངོ་མཚར་སྐྱེས། དེནས་རྒྱལ་བུས་ཀླུའི་ཞོར་བུ་རྣམས་བླ་མའི་སྤྱིལ་
བུར་ལྷ་གཅིག་ཀྱང་ལེན་པར་ཕྱིན་འཛིན། དེནས་ཕོ་བྲང་དུ་བཞེར་ཏེ།

༄༅། །ནོར་བུ་རྣམས་བླ་མའི་ཕྱག་ཏུ་ཕུལ་བས། བླ་མས་ཀྱང་
རྒྱལ་པོར་བསམ་འཕེལ་དང་། བློན་པོ་རྣམས་ལ་ནོར་བུ་སྣ་རེ་བཙས་གནང་
ངོ་། །དེར་རྒྱལ་པོས་ཁྱེད་རྒྱལ་བུ་ཆེན་པོ་ཡིན་པ་བདག་གིས་མ་ཤེས །
བླ་མའི་ཐུགས་དཀྲུགས་སྤུས་ཀྱི་སྐྱུ་ལ་བསྐྱོས་ལུས་ངག་ཡིད་གསུམ་
ཀྱི་སྡིག་སྒྲིབ་ཉེས་ལྟུང་ཐམས་ཅད་བཟོད་པར་བཞེས་ཤིང་མཐོལ་ལོ་
བ་ཤགས་སོ། །སྐྱེ་བ་ནས་ཚེ་རབས་ཏུ་རྗེས་སུ་བཟུང་ཞེས་གསོལ་ཏོ། །
དེ་ནས་གསེར་གྱི་ཁྲི་འཕང་མཐོ་བཞིག་བརྩེགས་པའི་སྟེང་གབ་རྩེ་གསུམ་
བརྩེགས་བྱས་པའི་སྟེང་དུ་བླ་མ་རིན་པོ་ཆེ་བཞུགས་སུ་གསོལ། །དངུལ་
གྱི་ཁྲི་འཕང་མཐོ་བའི་སྟེང་གབ་རྩེ་གཉིས་བརྩེགས་བཏིང་བའི་སྟེང་དུ་རྒྱལ་
བུ་དོན་ཐམས་ཅད་འགྲུབ་པ་བཞུགས་སུ་གསོལ། གཡུ་ཁྲིའི་སྟེང་གབ་རྩེ་
གཅིག་བཏིང་བའི་སྟེང་དུ་སྲས་མོ་ལྷ་གཅིག་འོད་ལྡན་དང་། རྒྱལ་པོ་རང་
གབ་རྩེ་འབོལ་གཉིས་བརྩེགས་བྱས། དེ་ནས་བསྙེན་བཀུར་ཕུན་སུམ་
ཚོགས་པ་ཞུས། དེ་ནས་རྒྱལ་པོ་གོ་ཆས་རྒྱལ་པོ་དོན་ཐམས་ཅད་འགྲུབ་
པ་འདི་རྒྱལ་པོའི་རིགས་གདུང་བརྒྱུད་ཚད་ཐུབ་པ་ཞིག་ཡིན་འདུག །ཁོང་
གི་མཛད་ལུགས་ཚོ་ཡང་རྫུ་འཕྲུལ་ལྟར་འདུག་པས་འཇིག་རྟེན་དུ་འདི་འདྲ་
འཚོལ་དུ་ཕྱིན་ཀྱང་མི་རྙེད་དེ། བུ་མོ་འདི་ཡང་ལས་ཀྱི་སྨོན་ལམ་གྱིས་རྒྱལ་
བུ་འདི་དང་འབྲལ་མི་ཐོད་པ་འདུག །བདག་ལ་རིགས་བརྒྱུད་ཀྱི་བུ་ནི་མེད་

༄༅། །ཕས༔ བདག་གི་རྒྱལ་ས་འདི་ཕོད་ལས་འོས་པ་མི···
འདུག་བླ་མའི་ཐུགས་དམ་ལ་ཇི་ལྟར་ཡོད་ཞུས་པས། རྒྱལ་པོ་བསོད···
ནམས་ཅན་ཚེད་དེང་ཡབ་ཡུམ་དང་སྨོན་ལམ་གྱི་འབྲེལ་བ་ཞིག་ཡིན།
བདག་གི་བུ་འདི་ཡང་འཕགས་པ་སྤྱན་རས་གཟིགས་ཀྱི་སྤྲུལ་པ་ཡིན་པས···
དེ་དག་ཐུགས་ལ་འབྲུངས་པ་ལགས་སོ་གསུངས་པས། གཞན་སྐར་མ···
ལ་སོགས་པ་བླ་མ་ཚེད་ལ་དྲིས་པས་ཞག་བཅུ་གསུམ་འདས་པའི་ཡར་ཚེས···
ལ་བཟང་བ་ཡིན་གསུངས། །དེར་རྒྱལ་པོ་དོན་ཐམས་ཅད་འགྲུབ་པ་འདི···
བདག་ཅག་རྒྱལ་པོ་གོ་ཆའི་རྒྱལ་སར་འདོན། བདག་ཀུང་རབ་ཏུ་བྱུང་ནས···
བླ་མ་དང་རང་རེ་གཉིས་རྩ་རྒྱུ་ཤིང་གསུམ་འཛོམས་པ་ཡུལ་གྱི་ཕུ་རི་ཁྲོད
ལེགས་པ་ཞིག་ལ་དགོན་པ་བཏབ་ནས་སྡོད་པ་ཡིན་གསུངས། དེ་ནས···
མངའ་འོག་གི་མགོ་བ་དཔོན་རྒྱལ་ཕྲན་སོགས་བསྡུས་ནས་རྒྱལ་སར···
རྒྱལ་བུ་དོན་ཐམས་ཅད་འགྲུབ་པ་འདོན་པ་ཡིན་པས། ཞག་བཅུ་གསུམ···
སོང་བའི་ཉིན་མོ་ཐམས་ཅད་ཀྱི་བཀུར་སྟི་ཕུ་དུད་འབུལ་བ་དང་བཅས···
ཁྲིར་ཤོག་གསུངས་པ་བརྡ་བཏང་། དེ་ནས་གཞན་སྐར་བཟང་འཛོམས···
ཉིན༔ རྒྱལ་པོ་བླ་མ། ཡུམ་མོ་ལྷ་གཅིག་བཅས་ཁྲི་སོ་སོར་བཞུགས···
འཚུག །དེ་ནས་རྒྱལ་པོས་ཡིད་བཞིན་གྱི་ནོར་བུ་མཆོག་ཕལ་མང་པོ···
དང་༔ རྟེན་གསུང་རྡོ་མཚར་བས་སྣ་དྲངས་གསེར་དང་པི་ཌཱུཪྻའི་སྒྲོགས་
པམ་

f 50

༄༅། །དར་ཟླབ་མང་པོ། །དངོས་པོ་གསེར་དངུལ་གྱི་དོང་རྩེ་མང་
པོ་སྣང་པོ་ཆེ་མང་པོ་ལ་བཀལ། རྟ་དང་མ་ཧེ་སོགས་ཇི་སྙེད་མང་པོ་
རྒྱལ་པོ་སྲས་མོ་གཉིས་ལ་ཕུལ། རྒྱལ་པོ་དོན་ཐམས་ཅད་འགྲུབ་པ་དང་
སྲས་མོ་ལྷ་གཅིག་འོད་ལྡན་གཉིས་ཡབ་ཡུམ་བྱས་ཏེ་རྒྱལ་སར་སྐོན།
དར་འཕྱུར་དུང་བུས། རོལ་མོ་དཀྲོལ། སྣ་དང་གར་སོགས་ཞག་མང་པོའི་
བར་བྱས་སོ། །དེའི་དུས་སུ་བློན་པོ་བརྒྱ་ཕྲག་གིས་ཞབས་ཏོག་ཉིན་རེ་བཞིན་
བློན་པོ་རེ་རེས་ཞུས་པས་ཉིན་བརྒྱའི་བར་དུ་སྦྲེལ། །བློན་པོ་ཏྲི་ཤུ་ནི་ད་དུང་
དད་པ་མ་སྐྱེས་ཅིང་སེམས་ལ་དགེ་སློང་ཁྲམ་སྐྱུལ་འདིས་སྒྱུ་མ་བྱས་པ་
འདྲ་བས་ཡིན་ཡང་ཁ་ཟུ་དང་མོས་ངོ་མཚར་ཡོད་པ་ལྟར་བྱས། ཉིན་རྗེས་
མཐས་བློན་པོ་ཏྲི་ཤུས། བླ་མ་རིན་པོ་ཆེ་རྒྱལ་པོ། །རྒྱལ་བུ་སོགས་ཚད་མ་
གདན་དྲངས་ཞག་གསུམ་གྱི་བར་དུ་བཀུར་སྟི་འབུལ་བ་ཕུན་སུམ་ཚོགས་
པ་ཞུས། དེར་རྒྱལ་བུས་ཆོས་གསུངས་པས་སེམས་ད་དུང་དད་པར་མ་གྱུར་
ཀྱང་། ཁ་ཟུ་བདག་ཉིད་ཀྱིས་འཁོར་དུ་སྐྱེ་བར་ཤོག་ཅིག་ཞུས། རྒྱལ་བུས་
ཀྱང་མ་འོང་པ་ན་དྲུང་དུ་འཁོད་པའི་གཙོ་བོ་ཡོང་ གསུངས་ཞལ་གྱིས་
བཞེས་སོ། །དེ་ནས་རྒྱལ་པོ་གོ་ཆས་བླ་མ་ལ་རབ་ཏུ་བྱུང་བའི་སྡོམ་པ་ཞུས།
འབངས་ནས་སྐྱེས་པ་བརྒྱ་ཕྲག་གསུམ་གྱིས་རབ་ཏུ་བྱུང་། ལྷུང་བའི་ཕུ་
རུ་དགོན་པ་ཅེད་འཕགས་ཞེས་བཏབ། འདིའི་མིང་བླ་མར་ཞུས་པས་སུ་

༄༅། །ཀར་ཞེས་བཏགས། བླ་མས་ཆོས་ཁྲིམས་དར་
གྱི་མདུད་པ་ལྷར་བསྒྲམས། བླ་མས་རྒྱལ་པོ་གོ་ཆ་དཔོན་གཡོག
བརྒྱ་ཕྲག་གསུམ་ལ་དགེ་སློང་བསྙེན་པར་རྫོགས་པ་གནང་། རྒྱལ་པོའི
ཆོས་མིང་དགེ་བ་དཔལ་ཞེས་བྱ་བ་དང་། གཞན་རྣམས་ལ་ཡང་ཆོས
མིང་རེ་བཏགས་པ་དེར་བླ་མ་དགེ་སློང་འཁོར་དང་བཅས་པ་དགོན་པར
བྱོན། རྒྱལ་པོ་ཡབ་ཡུམ་གྱིས་རྒྱལ་སྲིད་བསྐྱངས་པས་དར་ཞིང་རྒྱས
པ་ག་དགོ། །དེ་ནས་ལོ་གཉིས་སོང་ཙམ་ནནམ་ཞིག་རྒྱལ་པོ་དོན་ཐམས
ཅད་འགྲུབ་པའི་ཐུགས་དགོངས་ལ། བདག་ནི་རྒྱལ་སྲིད་ཆོས་བཞིན
དར་ཞིང་བླ་མ་དང་མཇལ། བདེ་སྐྱིད་ཕུན་སུམ་ཚོགས་ཀྱང་ནུ་བོ་དེ
ཤིན་རྟུལ་པ་ཆོལ། གསོན་ནམ་གར་འདུག་བལྟ། བླ་མའི་ལུང་བསྟན
བཟང་པོ་ཡོད་ཀྱང་ད་བར་ལུས། བདག་ཨ་ཇོ་སྣེ་རྟུལ་པོ་ཤུལ་དུ
ལུས་ན་ཙི་མི་བཏུབ་དགོངས་སྐྱོ་ཤས་ཆེན་པོ་སྐྱེས་སོ། །དེར་བློན་པོ
མང་དག་དང་བཅས་བསྡུས་ཏེ་ཏ་དང་གླང་པོ་ཟླ་བ་གཅིག་གི་ཡོ་བྱད
ཁྲབ་གྱིས། དེ་ངས་དཔོན་གཡོག་དར་ཞིང་རྒྱས་པའི་སྐབས་འདིར་སྐྱོ
བསངས་ལ་འགྲོ་ཡོ་བྱད་ཐང་ནགས་གསེབ་སོགས་ལ་བདེ་བར་སྐྱོད
དུ་འགྲོ་བ་ཡིན་གསུངས། དེར་ཁོང་རང་སྤུར་གར་བྱོན་པའི་ས་ཆ་དེད
དེ་བྱོན། ལུང་སྟོང་རྣམས་ལ་མི་གྲོད་བཟློས། ཞིང་སོགས་སློས་ཞིང

f 52

༄༅། །སློབ༔ ཆུ་མེད་པ་རྣམས་ལ་ཆུ་བཏོན། མངའ་རིག་དབུལ་···
འཕོངས་རྣམས་ལ་ཟས་ནོར་ས་ཞིང་གི་སྦྱིན་པ་རྒྱ་ཆེན་པོ་མཛད། དེར་རྒྱལ་
པོ་དོན་ཐམས་ཅད་འགྲུབ་པ་འཁོར་བཅས་ཀྱིས་རྒྱལ་བུ་དོན་ཡོད་གྲོངས་པའི་
ལ་དེར་ཐེབས། བློན་པོ་རྣམས་ཀྱིས་ཞུས་པ། སྤུར་མེད་པའི་གཟུགས་མི་
རུ་ཐུས་པ། ལུས་ལ་སྤུ་སྐྱེས་པའི་སྤྲེའུའི་ལུས་འདྲ་བཞིག་སྐད་ལྷང་ལྷང་
ལུང་པ་འདིའི་རི་སུལ་ཕ་གིར་གདའ་ལགས་ཞུས་པས་རྒྱལ་པོ་ནུ་བོ་དྲན་
ཏེ་ཐུགས་སྐྱོ། །དེར་རྒྱལ་པོས་ཁྱོད་རང་འབངས་འཁོར་དང་བཅས་པ་འདིར་
ལྷོངས་རྒྱུ་སོགས་གང་དགར་སྤྱོད་ཅིག །གཅིག་གི་གཅིག་ལ་དགའ་བ་དང་···
ལྡན་པར་གྱིས་བདག་འཁོར་དང་བཅས་པ་འཇག་ར་ཞིགས་ཕ་གིའི་རི་སུལ···
དབེན་པར་བྲུས་དང་ལྷོངས་རྒྱུར་འགྲོ་གསུངས། ཞབས་འབྲིང་པར་སུ····
ཁྲིད་དེ་ཚོན། དེ་ནས་ཕ་གིར་ཐེབས་པ་དང་དེ་རི་ང་ནུ་བོ་དང་མཇལ་བ་འདྲ····
དགོངས་དགྱེས་ཚོར་ཆེན་པོ་བྱུང་། དེ་ནས་སེམས་ཅན་འདུག་ཟེར་སར་
འགྲོ་ཡི་གསུངས་ཚེན་པ་ན། ལུང་པ་དེའི་རི་སུལ་ཕར་ལོགས་ཀྱི་ནགས་
ཀྱི་དཀྱིལ་ན་སྐད་ལྷང་ལྷང་ཞིག་འདུག་པར་གཞན་རྣམས། དེ་ཁར་སྤྱོད་
ཅིག་གསུངས་ཁོང་རང་གི་ག་ལེར་འཛབ་ཏེ་ཐེབས་པ་ན། མིའི་ལུས་ལ···
སྤུ་སྐྱེས་པ་ཡང་བ་ཞིག་རི་དྭགས་ཀྱི་ཤ་དང་ཤིང་ཏོག་ཁྱེར་ཏེ་ཨ་ཛི་དོན་···
འགྲུབ་གན་བཞུགས་ཡོད་པ་ཟེར། སྐད་འདོན་ཀྱི་ན་འདུག་གོ་དེར····

༄༅། །རྒྱལ་བུ་དོན་འགྲུབ་སྤྱན་ཆབ་ཤོར། ཁོ་ཤིན་པོ་རྣམས་ཀྱི་
བདག་ལ་འདི་འདྲ་བྱེད་རྩོན། བདག་ལས་ཁྱེར་ཁ་རྒྱང་བ་ཨེ་ཡོད་དགོངས་
སྙིང་ཤུགས་སྐྱེས་སོ། །དོན་ཡོད་དོན་ཡོད་བདག་འདིར་ཡོད་གསུངས་པ་ན།
ནུ་བོ་རྣ་མཆོག་ཐེབ་བེ་ཉན་འདུག་གོ །དེར་རྒྱལ་པོས་ཨ་ཇོ་འདི་རུ་ཡོད་……
ཟེར་ཙར་བྱོན་པ་ན། དེར་གཙུང་དོན་ཡོད་ཀྱི་བསམ་པ་ལ་བདག་གི་ཨ་ཇོའི་
གསུངས་ཡིན་འདུག་དགོངས་རྒྱུགས་བྱོན་སྐུ་མཆེད་གཉིས་པོ་གཅིག་གིས་…
གཅིག་གི་མྱུག་ནས་འཛུལ་ནས། རྒྱལ་བུས་བདག་གི་ནུ་བོ་འདི་འདྲ་ཡོང་བ་……
གསུངས། ནུ་བོས་ཨ་ཇོ་རང་མཇལ་ཟེར་དགའ་བྲགས་གཉིས་ཀས་བཀྲུམས་
སོ། །དེ་ནས་ནུ་བོའི་སྐྲ་རྣམས་སྐྲ་གྲིས་བྲེགས། བྱིངས་སྤྱོད་ལས་རང་ཕེབས་ཏེ་
རྒྱལ་བུ་སྐུ་མཆེད་མཇལ་ཏེ་སྐྱོབ་བསངས་པས་སྐྱོབ་བསངས་ཞེས་པའི་ལོ་……
རྒྱུས་དེ་ནས་བྱུང་ངོ་། །གཙུང་པོའི་སྐུ་ལུས་ཀྱི་སྤུ་ལྤགས་མ་རྣམས་ཀྱང་སྤུ་གྲིས་
བཞར། བདུད་རྩི་རྣམ་པ་ལྔ་ཞལ་དུ་བྲངས་པས་ཨ་ཇོ་དང་གཟིམ་དངས་……
མཉམ་ལ་ཁད་ཙམ་བྱུང་། རྒྱལ་བུ་གྲོ་བླ་པའི་ས་ཆ་དེར་རྒྱུག་ཡས་གཡོན་ནས་
དྲངས་ཏེ་རྫིང་སྐྱེལ། །དགོན་སྡེ་བཙུགས། དགེ་བ་རྒྱུན་མི་ཆད་པར་བྱས་སོ། །
བྱོན་པའི་ལམ་ཁ་ལ་ཡང་ཡུལ་གྲོ་འཛོག་པའི་འཛག་བཀོད་མཛད། དེ་ནས་
ཕོ་བྲང་ལ་སྤྱི་མཇོགས་པ་བཏང་། གཙུང་དོན་ཡོད་ཤི་བ་གསོས་པའི་ལོ་……
རྒྱུས་རྣམས་ཞུས་པས་དེར་འཁོར་ཐམས་ཅད་ཧ་ལས་ངོ་མཚར་སྐྱེས། དེ་…

f 54

༄༅། །ནས་སྐུ་མཆེད་གཉིས་འཁོར་དང་བཅས་པ་ཕོ་བྲང་དུ་ལོག་
ཕྱིན་པས། སྲས་མོ་ལྷ་གཅིག་འོད་ལྡན་གྱི་དབུ་མཛད། མོ་སྐྱེས་མང་པོ་དང་
བཅས་བསུ་བ་ལ་ཕྱིན་ནོ། །ཕོ་བྲང་ལ་དར་འཕྱུར་རོལ་མོ་དཔག་ཏུ་མེད་པ་ཕྱས།
ཕྲོ་དང་ཞོན་སོགས་རྗེད་སྣ་མང་པོ་གནམ་ལ་སྤྱིར་བ་ལྟར་བྱུང་ངོ། །བླ་མ་དང་
རྒྱལ་པོ་དགེ་བ་དཔལ་ལ་ཀུང་གདན་དྲངས། ཀུན་དོ་མཚར་ཞིང་དད་པ་སྐྱེས །
དེའི་དུས་སུ་ཡང་བློན་པོ་ཏྲི་ཤུས་བསམ་པ་ལ། བླ་མ་དགེ་སློང་ཁྲམ་སྐྱེལ་འདིའི་
མིག་འཕྲུལ་སྒྱུ་མའི་ཐབས་ཀྱི་ཁོང་རང་གི་བུ་ལ་རྒྱལ་ས་ཕྱོབ་པ་ཕྱས། དེས་ཀྱང་
མི་ཆོག་ནུ་བོ་མཐའ་ལ་འཁྱམས་པ་དེ་ཡང་ཐབས་ཀྱིས་བཀུག་ནས་ཁོང་སྤུན་
གཉིས་མཉམ་དུ་འཛོག་པ་འདུག་པས། ངའི་བདག་བློན་པོའི་དཀྱིལ་གྱི་གོ་
ཆོད་དྲག་ཙམ་འཛོམས་པ་ཞིག་ཡིན་ཀྱང་། ཁོང་ཕ་མང་ཀྱི་དེ་གོང་གི་སྙིང་
ནད་ཀྱིས་བདེ་རུ་འཚུག་མི་ཡོང་བསམ་དོགས་པ་ཞིག་ཀྱང་སྐྱེས། དེ་ནས་
རྒྱལ་པོ་དོན་ཐམས་ཅད་འགྲུབ་པ་སྐུ་མཆེད་གཉིས་ལ་གསེར་ཁྲི་རེ། །བླམས་
བཀྲ་ཤིས་མངའ་གསོལ་རབ་གནས་སོགས་མཛད་དོ། །དགའ་སྟོན་ཀྱང་ལོ་
བདུན་གྱི་བར་དུ་མཛད་དོ། །དེ་ནས་བློན་པོ་ཏྲི་ཤུ་བསམ་ངན་སྐྱེས་ཏེ། གཏྲ་པ་
ཏ་ཞེས་པའི་ཡུལ་གྱི་ལྡོངས་བཟུང་ཐག་གི་ཇག་དཔོན་དང་གྲོགས་བྱས་ནས
དམག་རྒྱག་ཕྱོགས་པར་ བར། རྒྱལ་བུ་དོན་ཡོད་ཀྱིས་དམག་དཔོན་བྱས་ཏེ་འཐུལ།
བློན་པོ་འཁྲིད་ཕྱིན་ཏེ་སྐུ་མཆེད་གཉིས་ཀར་བཟློད་པ་གསོལ་བས། །སྔར་གྱི་

ཆོས་བློན་ཛ་ཡ་རྡ་ར་དང་། ཨོ་ནན་ཏ། ལས་ཀྱི་བློན་པོ་ཏྲི་ཤུ་བཅས་ པས་ཕྱག་དྲངས།
པོ་སྐྱེས་མང་པོ་བརྒྱན་བཟང་པོ་དང

༄༅། །ཀྱི་གཞིས་ལས་གསུམ་འགྱུར་གྱི་རྒྱ་ཆེ་བ་བསྐལ་བས······
ཡིད་ཆེས། འོན་ཀྱང་དད་པའི་སེམས་མ་སྐྱེས་སོ། །ཆབ་འབངས་ཐམས···
ཅད་བདེ་བ་ལ་འཁོད་དེ་མཐའི་རྒྱལ་པོ་རྣམས་ཀྱིས་ཀྱང་ཕྱག་འབུལ་དུ······
འོངས། དེར་རྒྱལ་པོ་དོན་ཐམས་ཅད་འགྲུབ་པའི་ཐུགས་དགོངས་ལ་ཟླ་མའི···
ཞབས་ཏོག་སྒྲུབ། ཧུ་བོ་དང་ཡང་ཤི་གསོན་འཕྲད། སློན་ལམ་བཏབ་ཚོད་ཐོབ
ཕྱིར་; དཞི་ཡབ་ཡུམ་གཉིས་མཇལ་དུ་འགྲོ་དགོངས་ཏེ། གཙུང་དང་བཙུན···
མོ་ལ་གྲོས་ཕྱས་མཛད་པས་ལེགས་སོ་བརྗོད་དོ། །ཆོས་བློན་དཔལ་འབར···
དང་བློན་པོ་ཧྲི་ཤུ་རྒྱལ་པོ་གོ་ཆའི་པོ་བྲང་དུ་བཞག་ནས། དེར་ཡིད་བཞིན་གྱི···
ནོར་བུས་ཐོག་བྲངས་པའི་རིན་པོ་ཆེ་སྣ་བདུན་དང་། གསེར་དངུལ་ཡོ་ཕྱད·····
སོགས་རྒྱལ་སྲིད་ཀྱི་བཅའ་པ་མང་པོ་སྣང་ཆེན་གྱི་རྒྱབ་ཁལ་མང་པོ་དང་།
ཡབ་ཡུམ་གསུམ་ལ་འཁོར་ཆོས་བློན་ཛྙ་ཡ་དྷར། ཨ་ནན་ཏས་ཕྱོག་གྲངས་
བློན་པོ་སྟོང་ཕྲག་གཅིག་གི་ཚོགས་དང་བཅས་བྱོན་ནོ། །དེ་ནས་རྒྱལ་པོའི·····
གྲོང་གསར་རྒྱུག་བྱེད་མིས། ཡབ་ཡུམ་གྱི་ས་ཆའི་ཁྲིད་ཉེར་མཁར་ལས···
བྱེད་པས། མཐའི་རྒྱལ་པོ་དྲག་ཆེན་དེས་རང་རེའི་རྒྱལ་ས་འཕྲོག་པ་འདྲ···
ཟེར་གཏམ་ཐོས་པས་ཡ་ང་བ་དང་། རྒྱལ་པོ་སྐུ་མཆེད་མེད་པའི་རྒྱུ་ངན····
ཡང་སངས་དུས་མ་བྱུང་བར་ཡབ་ཡུམ་ཐུགས་ཁྲལ་གྱིས་བཞུགས་ཡོད་པ···
ལ། རྒྱལ་བུ་སྐུ་མཆེད་ཀྱི་ཡབ་ཡུམ་གྱི་པོ་བྲང་ལ་པོ་ཉ་སྤ་མགྱོགས་པ་བརྒྱ···

༄༅། །ཁྲག་གཅིག་བཏང་བས་འབངས་ཐམས་ཅད་དམག་བྱུང་
ཟེར་འུར་ཤོག་ཆེན་པོ་བྱུང་ངོ་། །དེ་ནས་ཆོས་བློན་ཛ་ཡ་ཧྲ་ར་དཔོན་གཡོག
ལྔས་ཕོ་བྲང་དུ་ཕྱིན་ཏེ། རྒྱལ་བུ་དོན་ཐམས་ཅད་འགྲུབ་པ་དང་དོན་ཡོད
སྐུ་མཆེད་བཙུན་མོ་དང་བཅས་ཡབ་ཡུམ་མཇལ་བར་ཕེབས་པས་ཞུ་བ
འབུལ་མི་ཡིན་ཟེར་ཞུས་པས། དེ་འདྲག་ལ་སྦྲིད། རྒྱལ་པོ་གོ་ཆས་ངེད་ཀྱི
རྒྱལ་ས་འཕྲོག་རྒྱུ་ཡིན་འདུག་གསུངས། བློན་འབངས་དང་བཅས་པ་སྐྲག
ནས་ཅི་དྲག་ལ་ཐུག །དེ་ནས་ཡབ་ཡུམ་གྱི་ཕོ་བྲང་ཉེ་འདབ་ཐང་ཞིག་ཏུ་སྒར
གྲལ་བསྒྲིགས་ཏེ་ཞག་གཅིག་བཞུགས། དེ་ནས་བློན་པོ་དཔོན་གཡོག་ལྔ
བཅས་ཕོ་ཉ་ཡབ་ཡུམ་གྱི་སར་བཏང་བའི་བཀའ་ཤོག་གི་སྒྲོམ་བུར་སྐུ་མཆེད
མཐའ་ལ་བཙུགས་ཤིང་ངོ་རྒྱལ་འབྱུང་ལུགས་བསྐུར། དེ་རྗེས་དཔོན་གཡོག
ལྔ་བཏང་བའི་བཀའ་ཤོག་ལ། བཙུན་དོན་ཡོད་གྲོངས་ལུགས་དང་བླ་མ
སྐུ་དྲིན་ཅན་དང་མཇལ་ལུགས་བསྐུར། ཕོ་ཉ་རྗེས་མའི་བཀའ་ཤོག་ལ
གཙུང་པོ་ཤི་གསོ་མཇལ་ལུགས། ཀླུ་ཡུལ་དུ་ཕྱིན་ལུགས་དང་། རྒྱལ་པོ
གོ་ཆའི་རྒྱལ་ས་བཟུང་ལུགས་སོགས་བསྐུར་ཏེ་ཕོ་ཉ་སྔ་གཏིང་གསུམ
བཏང་བས་ཡབ་ཡུམ་བློན་འབངས་དང་བཅས་ཧ་ལས་ངོ་མཚར་སྐྱེས་ཤིང་
དགའ་བ་ཚད་མེད་པ་བྱུང་ངོ་། །དེ་མ་ཐག་ནམ་མཁའ་དར་གྱིས་བཀང་། ས
གཞི་གླུ་གར་རོལ་མོ་སྟེད་འཛིའི་སྒྲ་ལ་སོགས་པས་བཀང་། ཡབ་རྒྱལ་པོ

༄༅། །ཀླུ་ལ་དེ་ཕ་སྤུར་པོ་བྲང་གི་རྒྱལ་སྒྲོ་འགོམས་མ།
སྒྲོངས་ཀྱང་ཕྲུག་ལ་གཡུའི་མཁར་བ་བསྐྲམས་ནས་བདག་གི་བུ་གཉིས
དང་མཉན་འ་བླ་ཙཀྵ་འཕྲད་དུ་འགྲོ་ཡི་གསུངས་ཏེ། བློན་པོ་མང་པོའི་ཚོགས
དང་བཅས་བསུ་བ་ལ་བྱོན་ཏེ། རྒྱལ་བུ་སྐུ་མཆེད་གཉིས་བཙུན་མོ་དང་
བཅས་པའི་གཟིམ་གུར་གྱི་འགག་ཏུ་ཕྲག་བརྟེན་དང་བཅས་ཡབ་ཡུམ
མཇལ་བར་ཞུས། དགྱེས་དགྱེས་གྲགས་པས་གཅིག་གཅིག་ལ་འཁྱུད་སོ།།
དེ་ནས་སྨར་ཕྲོག་ཏུ་ཞག་གསུམ་བཞུགས། ས་དེ་ཡང་བཀྲ་ཤིས་རྟགས་བརྒྱད
ཀྱི་རྣམ་པར་འདུག །ཡུམ་ལྷ་གཅིག་པདྨ་ཅན་གྱི་ནོར་བུ་བསམ་འཕེལ
དང་། ཀ་ཀེ་ཏུ་དང་། མཐོན་ཀ་དང་། བེ་ཌཱུརྱ་དང་། མ་རྒད་ཨི་ནྡྲ་ནཱི་ལ
དང་ནོར་སྣ་མང་ཡོད། ནོར་བུ་ཆ་བདུན་དང་། རྟ་དང་གླང་པོ་ཆེ་གོས་དར
སོགས་ཀྱི་འབུལ་ཚན་དཔག་ཏུ་མེད་པ་ཕུལ་ཞིང་ཕྱག་བཙལ་ལོ། ཆོས
ཀྱི་རྒྱལ་པོ་དོན་ཐམས་ཅད་འགྲུབ་པ་ཁྱེད་ཀྱི་ཛཱ་འཕྲུལ་བདག་གིས་མ་གོ། །
ང་རྒྱལ་སྒྲིར་རྒྱུ་བ་བསམ་ངན་ཐལ་བ་བཟོད་པ་བཞེས། དེད་རྐན་གོ་ག་གཉིས
ཀྱི་སྐྱིད་སྡུག་ཁྱེད་སྐུ་མཆེད་གཉིས་ཀྱིས་མཁྱེན་གསུངས་ཏེ། སྤྱན་ཆབ
དང་ཕྲག་མང་དུ་བཙལ་ཞིང་ཞབས་སྤྱི་བོར་བླངས་སོ། །དེར་རྒྱལ་པོ་དོན
ཐམས་ཅད་འགྲུབ་པས་བཀའ་སྩལ་བ། ༔ །བདག་རིགས
དྲུག་ཕ་མར་ཤེས་པ་ལ། །ཁོན་དང་ཞེ་འཛིན་ག་ལ་ཡོད། ཕྲག་དོག་རྣམ

༄༅། །རྟོག་ཀུན་གྲོལ་བས། །ཉེ་དང་རིང་བ་ག་ལ་ཡོད། །ཨ་མས
གར་མཛད་གྲོགས་སུ་བྱུང་། །ཞེས་གསུངས་པས་ཡབ་ཡུམ་སློབ་འབངས་
ཐམས་ཅད་ཡིད་ཆེས་ཀྱི་དད་པ་ཐོབ་བོ། །དེ་ནས་སློབ་འབངས་འཁོར་དང་
བཅས་ཡབ་ཡུམ་གྱི་ཕོ་བྲང་བཀྲ་ཤིས་བརྩེགས་པར་ཕྱག་ཕེབས། རྒྱལ་པོ་
དོན་ཡོད་ཡབ་རྒྱལ་པོའི་རྒྱལ་སར་མངའ་གསོལ་ཞིང་། སྐུ་མཆེད་གཉིས་
རྒྱལ་ས་སྔན་ཚུན་ཁྱད་མེད་ཅིང་བཙུན་མོ་ཡང་གཅིག་གིས་ལྷུས་པ་མཛད།
ཆབ་འབངས་ཐམས་ཅད་དར་ཞིང་རྒྱས་པ་འཛམ་གླིང་གསུམ་གཉིས་ཀྱི་
བདག་པོར་གྱུར་ཏོ། །སློབ་པོ་དྲི་ཤུ་དམག་དཔོན་ལ་བསྐོས་ཏེ་མཐའ་བཞིའི་
རྒྱལ་ཕྲན་ཐམས་ཅད་དང་ཤུགས་ཀྱིས་ཆབ་འོག་ཏུ་བསྡུས། ནམ་ཞིག་རྒྱལ་
པོ་དོན་ཐམས་ཅད་འགྲུབ་པས། བདག་གི་ལྷ་མ་བཀའ་འདྲིན་ཅན་དང་། རྒྱལ་
པོ་དགེ་བ་དཔལ་འབར་གདན་འདྲེན་གྱི་ཕོ་ཉ་གཏོང་དགོས་གསུངས་ཏེ
མངགས། བླ་མ་རིན་པོ་ཆེ་དང་རྒྱལ་པོ་དགེ་བ་དཔལ་དགེ་འདུན་ཁྲི་ཕྲག་
གསུམ་དང་བཅས་པ་ཕོ་བྲང་དུ་ཕེབས། ཕོ་བྲང་བཀྲ་ཤིས་བརྩེགས་པར་
གུང་གི་གསེར་ཁྲི་ཆེན་པོར་བླ་མ་ལེགས་པའི་བློ་གྲོས་བཞུགས། དེའི་
གཡས་སུ་དངུལ་ཁྲི་བརྩེགས་ཏེ་རྒྱལ་པོ་དགེ་བ་དཔལ། ཡབ་རྒྱལ་པོ་ཟླ་ལ་
དེ་ཕྱ་ཡུམ་པདྨ་ཅན་རྣམས་བཞུགས། གཡོན་དུ་གསེར་ཁྲི་བརྩེགས་པ་
ལ་རྒྱལ་པོ་དོན་ཐམས་ཅད་འགྲུབ་པ་བཞུགས། །དངུལ་ཁྲི་གཅིག་ལ་རྒྱལ་

f 59

༄༅། །པོ་ཏོ་ཡོད་བཞུགས། གཡུ་ཁྲི་གཅིག་ལ་བཙུན་མོ་དོན་
ལྷན་མ་རྣམས་གྲལ་མཛད། དེར་གྲོམ་པ་བློ་གྲོས་ཡེ་ཤེས་ཏོག །རྒྱལ་
མཚན་དཔལ། ཉི་མས་སྦྱིན་སོགས་དང་བཅས་དགེ་འདུན་གྱི་འཁོར་ཁྲི་
ཕྲག་མང་པོ་དང་། མོ་མ་ཀ་ཧྲེ་དང་མཚན་མཁན་ཟླ་ཏྲ་སོགས་བྲམ་ཟེ་མང་
པོ་དང་། ཆོས་ཀྱི་བློན་པོ་ཆོས་དཔལ་འབར་དང་། ཛ་ཡ་ཧྲར། ཨནན་ཧྲ།
ཟླ་བས་ཕྱིན། ཀ་ཧྲེ་ཀ་སོགས་འཁོར་བློན་པོ་ཁྲི་ཕྲག་མང་པོ་དང་བཅས་
ཐབས་གཅིག་ཏུ་བཞུགས་ཏེ། དགའ་སྟོན་བསམ་གྱི་མི་ཁྱབ་པར་
མཛད་དོ། །དེ་ནས་ཟླ་བ་གསུམ་དང་ཞག་བཅུ་ཕྲག་གཉིས་ཀྱི་བར་དུ་ཟླ་
མས་རྒྱུ་འབྲས་ཀྱི་རྣམ་གཞག་གཙོ་བོར་གྱུར་པའི་ཆོས་གསུངས་རྒྱལ་
བུ་དོན་ཐམས་ཅད་འགྲུབ་པའི་རྣམ་ཐར་མཛད་པ་ངོ་མཚར་ཅན་མང་པོ་
བརྗོད་ནས། དེའི་མཇུག་ཏུ་རང་ཅག་རྣམས་མ་འོངས་སྙིགས་མའི་དུས་
སུ་འདི་ནས་བྱང་གི་ཕྱོགས་དཔག་ཚད་བརྒྱ་ཕྲག་གཉིས་ཙམ་པའི་ཕ་
རོལ་འདྲེ་སྲིན་གཅན་གཟན་དུ་མས་གང་བའི་ཡུལ་དམ་ཆོས་ཀྱི་སྣ་མི་
གྲགས་ཅིང་མཐའ་འཁོབ་གངས་རིའི་ལྗོངས་ཟེར་བ་ཞིག །དེ་བཞིན་
གཤེགས་པ་གོ་ཏ་མ་ཞེས་པ་འཇིག་རྟེན་དུ་འབྱུང་བའི་དུས་སུ་ཡོང་།
དེང་སང་ཉི་མཚོའི་ངང་བུ་བཞིན་དུ་ཡོད། དེ་བཞིན་གཤེགས་པ་དེའི་བསྟན་པ་
ལ་མཐའ་འཁོབ་དེ་ལྷ་སྲུང་རམིའི་འགྲོ་བ་ཆགས་ཏེ་དམ་པའི་ཆོས་དར་ཞིང་

༄༅། །ཁྲུས་པ་འབྱུང་། དེ་རྒྱལ་བུ་དོན་ཐམས་ཅད་འགྲུབ་པ་
ཁྱེད་ཀྱི་འདུལ་བའི་ཞིང་ཡིན། ཞིང་དེ་ན་ཁྱོད་ཐོག་མར་རྒྱལ་པོ་བཙན་
གྱི་མིང་ཅན་སྐྱེ་བ་གསུམ་མམ་བདུན་ཙམ་དུ་བླངས་ནས། དམ་པའི་
ཆོས་དབུ་བརྙེས་སྒྲོལ་གཙུགས། དེ་རྣམས་ཀྱི་དུས་སུ་གཙུང་དོན་ཡོད་
ཁྱེད་ཕལ་ཆེར་སྤྲུས་སུ་འགྱུར་ཞིང་། བདག་ནི་གཅིག་གཉིས་ཕ་དང་
ཕལ་ཆེར་བླ་མཆོད་དགེ་སློང་གི་ཚུལ་བཟུང་སྟེ་འགྲོ་བ་མང་པོའི་དོན་
བྱེད། དེ་ཡང་བསྟན་པ་ཙུང་ཟད་ཉམས་པ་ན་བདག་འཕགས་ཡུལ་དུ
བྱང་ཆུབ་སེམས་དཔའ་དེ་པཾ་ཀ་ར་ཞེས་པར་འགྱུར་ཏེ། ཁ་ཙན་དུ་མཁན་པོ
བྱེད། བུ་དོན་ཐམས་ཅད་འགྲུབ་པ་ཛ་ཡའི་མིང་ཅན་དུ་འགྱུར་ཏེ་སྤྲས་ཀྱི་ཐུ
བོར་འགྱུར། གཙུང་དོན་ཡོད་ཁྱོད་བདག་གི་པྲཛྙའི་མིང་ཅན་དུ་འགྱུར་ཏེ
འགྲོ་བའི་དོན་དཔག་ཏུ་མེད་པ་བྱེད་ཅིང་བསྟན་པ་ཁྱོས། བརྗོད་དུས་སྙིགས་
མ་ཐ་མའི་དུས། ངཅག་གཉིས་མཁན་སློབ་ཡབ་སྲས་འབྲལ་བ་མེད།
གཙུང་ཁྱོད་ཀྱང་སྦྱིན་བདག་རྒྱལ་པོའི་ཚུལ་གྱིས་འགྲོ་བའི་དོན་བྱེད། ལ་ལ་
ནི་འཁོར་ལོས་སྒྱུར་བའི་རྒྱལ་པོར་སྐྱེས་ཏེ་སྦྱིན་བདག་གི་ཚུལ་གྱིས་དགེ་
འདུན་མང་པོའི་ཚོགས་དཔོན་བྱས་ཏེ་འགྲོ་བ་མང་པོའི་འདྲེན་པ་བྱེད།
ལ་ལ་ནི་ཡབ་ཡུམ་གྱི་ཚུལ། དེ་རྣམས་ཀྱི་དུས་ཁྱེད་འདིར་ཚོགས་སྐལ་
བར་ལྡན་པ་རྣམས་ལ་ལ་ནི་རྒྱལ་ཆབ་མཁན་པོ་དང་སློབ་བུའི་ཚུལ་གྱིས་

༄༅། །དགེ་འདུན་མང་པོའི་ཚོགས་དཔོན་བྱས་ཏེ་འགྲོ་བ་
མང་པོའི་འདྲེན་པ་བྱེད། ལ་ལ་ནི་ཡབ་ཡུམ་གྱི་ཚུལ་བཟུང་སྟེ་སློན་
ལམ་གྱི་མཐུ་ཐོབ། ལ་ལ་ནི་འཁོར་ལོས་བསྒྱུར་བའི་རྒྱལ་པོར་སྐྱེས་
ཏེ་སྦྱིན་བདག་གི་ཚུལ་བྱེད། ལ་ལ་ནི་དད་བཞིན་མཁས་གྲུབ་མཛད་དེ་
བུ་སློབ་ཏུ་འགྱུར། ལ་ལ་སྐྱེ་བ་རིགས་དམན་ཀྱང་བདག་ཡབ་སྲས་ཀྱི་
ཞལ་མཐོང་གསུང་ཐོས་ཏེ་དད་པ་ཐོབ་ནས་བྱང་ཆུབ་ཀྱིས་ཟིན་པར་འགྱུར་
ཏོ༔ ༔ཞེས་མ་འོངས་ཀྱི་ལུང་བསྟན་ཀྱང་བཀའ་གནང་ངོ་། དེར་ཚོགས་
ཚང་མ་ངོ་མཚར་སྐྱེས་ཡིད་ཆེས་ཏེ་བླ་མ་ཡབ་སྲས་གསུམ་ལ་ཕྱག་
བཙལ། མཆོད་པ་ཕུལ་བརྟེན་བཅས་རང་རང་གི་གློས་གང་བཙོགས་
ཕུལ༔ བློན་པོ་ཏྲི་ཤུ་ནི་ད་དུང་ལོག་ལྟ་མཆག་སྟེ་ང་རྒྱལ་པོ་གོ་ཆའི་ཕོ་
བྲང་ལ་སྡོད་པ་ལ་བློན་པོ་ཆོས་དཔལ་འབར་གྱིས་མ་ཤེས་པ་བྱས།
ཇག་མི་བརྒྱ་ཕྲག་གཅིག་འཁྲིད་དེ་བློན་པོའི་བསམ་པར་བླ་མ་ཁྲམ་པ་
སྒྱུ་མ་མཁན་དེས། བུ་གཉིས་རྒྱལ་པོ་ཕན་ཚུན་གྱི་རྒྱལ་ས་རང་ཤུགས་
ཀྱིས་ལེན་བཅུག །བླ་མ་ཕབ་ལ་བརྡེས་ནའང་མི་ཐུབ་མཐའ་ལ་བྱོལ་འགྲོ་
བསམ་ཏེ་ཕྱིན་པས་ལམ་འཕྲང་ཞིག་ཏུ་རི་ཉིལ་ནས་ཚེའི་དུས་བྱས་སོ། །
དེའི་དུས་སུ་རྒྱལ་འབངས་ཐམས་ཅད་དར་ཞིང་རྒྱས། དགེ་འདུན་གྱི་སྡེ་
མང་པོ་འཕེལ། བདེ་སྐྱིད་ལྷ་ཡུལ་ལ་འདྲེན་པ་རྒྱལ་རབ་མང་པོའི་བར་

༄༅། །དུ་བྱུང་ངོ། །རྒྱལ་པོ་སྤྱན་རས་གཟིགས་དོན་ཐམས་ཅད་···
འགྲུབ་པའི་རྣམ་ཐར་རྟོགས་བརྗོད་གསང་བའི་ལུང་བྱོགས་སོ།།
འདིའི་ལོ་རྒྱུས་སྐལ་ལྡན་དང་བཅན་ལམ་གཏེགས་གཞན་ལ་བསྟན་ན་སྐལ་···
མེད་ལོག་ལྟའི་ལམ་གྱིས་དགྲོལ་བར་བསྒྱུར་བའི་ཉེན་ཡོད་པས་དང་ལྡན་···
པན་རྫུན་ལ་སྟོན་པ་ལས་ཁྱེངས་ལ་ཤིན་ཏུ་གསང་བ་གལ་ཆེའོ།། ཨོཾ།།
༔ །།དེའི་ཚེ་དེའི་དུས་ཀྱི་རྒྱལ་པོ་དོན་ཐམས་ཅད་འགྲུབ་བ་དེ། ད་ལྟའི་སྐུ་ཞབས་
རྒྱལ་དབང་མཆོག་འདི་ཉིད་ཡིན། དེ་དུས་ཀྱི་བླ་མ་ལེགས་པའི་བློ་གྲོས་ནི་ང···
ཅག་ཡིན། དེའི་དུས་ཀྱི་རྒྱལ་པོ་གོ་ཆ་དེ་སྡེ་པ་གོང་མ་ཡིན། དེའི་དུས་ཀྱི་བློན་པོ···
ཏི་ཤུ་དེ་ད་ལྟའི་སྡེ་པ་འདི་ཉིད་ཡིན། དེའི་དུས་ཀྱི་རྒྱལ་པོ་དོན་འགྲུབ་ཀྱི···
ཡུམ་དེ་ད་ལྟའི་ཡུམ་དུ་བྱུར་པ་ཡིན། དེའི་དུས་ཀྱི་ལམ་ལ་སླུལ་ལོག་ལྟ···
སྒྲིས་པ་དགུ་པོ་ཀུང་གཅིག་ཙམ་ང་ཅག་གི་དྲུང་ཁྲིད་ན་ཡོད་ཅིང་། །གཞན···
རྣམས་རྗེ་ཤོད་ཀྱི་སྐུ་ཞབ་ས་སུ་འཁོད་པ་འགའ་འཞིག་ཀྱང་གནོད་མི་ཐུབ···
བཀའ་གནང་ངོ། །སྔར་ཡང་མྱུག་བཙལ་ཏེ། དེའི་དུས་ཀྱི་གཞན་རྣམས···
ད་ལྟ་ཤེ་ཡོད་ཞུས་པས། ཡོད་པེབས་གཞལ་གསལ་མི་གནང་ཀྱང་།
སྔར་སྨྲུ་རནས་ཞུས་པས། གཞན་ཡང་དེའི་དུས་ཀྱི་གཙུང་དོན་ཡོད་དེ་ད···
ལྟའི་དབྱིངས་ས་བར་པའི་སྲུས་སྡེ་པ་ཨ་བར་འདི་ཡིན་པར་སེམས།
ཆོས་བློན་ཨ་ནན་རྡར་དབྱིངས་ས་བ་ར་པ་ཡིན་པར་སེམས། ཇོ་ཀ་ལ···

༄༅། །ཤིང་ཀ་གཞིས་ནི་དེ་མོ་སྤྲུལ་སྐུ་དང་ཕྱུགས་ཆེན་འདི་ཉིད་
ཡིན་པར་སེམས། མོ་ས་ཀ་རྡོ་ནི་བློ་བ་བཟང་འཛམས་པ་འདི་ཉིད་ཡིན། ཀ་ལན་
ཏ་ཀ་ནི་རྗེ་བཙུང་བློ་བཟང་ནོར་བུ་ཡིན། དེའི་དུས་ཀྱི་ཕྲེང་ཐུབ་སྨོན་ལམ་འདེབས
པ་དེ་ད་ལྟའི་སྟེར་སྟོན་དར་རྒྱས་སྤྲིངས་(ཚེ་ས)པ་ཡིན། བློན་པོ་དཔལ་འབར་ནི་
ཁྲག་མདོད་ཕུན་ཚོགས་རབ་བརྟན་ཡིན། ཆོས་བློན་ཛ་ཡ་རྡྷ་ར་ནི་རྣམ་
རྒྱལ་གྲྭ་ཚང་གི་སྤྱི་པ་སྤྱིན་པ་ཡིན། མཆན་མཁན་ཟླ་དྲ་ནི་དཔྱ་མཛད་
ཆོས་རྒྱ་མཚོ་ཡིན། ཆོས་བློན་རབ་བརྟན་དེ་ད་ལྟའི་གསོལ་དཔོན་
ཡིན༑ ཟླ་བས་བྱིན་ནི་གཞུང་སའི་བཀའ་བློན་རག་ཀྲུ་གནས་ཡིན། སྐྱ་
དང་སྤྲེ་ཝུའི་སྨོན་ལམ་འདེབས་པའི་སྐྱ་དེ་རྒྱལ་པོ་རྡ་ལག་བཏུར་ཡིན།
སྤྲེ་ལུ་དེ་མདའ་རིགས་ཞལ་ཕྱུགས་ཡིན། ཡབ་རྒྱལ་པོ་ཟླ་ལ་དེ་བ་དེ་ཉིད་
བསྟན་འཛིན་ཆོས་རྒྱལ་ཡིན། ཆོས་བློན་ཀ་རྟེ་ཀ་ནི་ད་ལྟའི་རྒྱལ་པོ་ཁྲི་
པ་ཡིན༑ ཕུམ་པདྨ་ཅན་ནི་ད་ལྟའི་གཡོན་སྲུན་བས་དྲུང་ཡིན། རྒྱལ་
པོ་གོ་ཆའི་སྲས་མོ་དེ་ནི་ཁྲི་རིན་པོ་ཆེ་སྒྲིང་ཡག་པ་ཡིན། སྤྲེག་པ་གཡོག་
ལྟ་སྐྱེས་ནས་སྨོན་ལམ་འདེབས་པ་ནི། དགེ་སློང་གི་ཚུལ་བཟུང་ད་ལྟ་
ང་ཅག་དང་གངས་ཐམས་ཅད་མཁྱེན་པར་སེལ་འཛུགས་ཞུ་བའི་སྐུ་ལ་
བཅར་བ་ཞིག་ཡིན། ཤང་ཤང་གཉིས་ནི་རྒྱ་ནག་པོག་རྗེ་དང་། ཧོར་
དེའི་རྒྱལ་པོ་ཡིན། བྱ་རི་དྭགས་ཀྱི་བསྐོར་བ་བྱེད་པ་དེ་དག་ཀྱང་སྐྱིན་

༄༅། །བདག་རྒྱལ་པོར་གྱུར་ཏོ། ང་ཅག་ཡབ་སྲས་ལ་དང་
པ་བྱེད་པའི་དཔྲའི་བྱང་ཕྱོགས་རྒྱལ་ཕྲན་མང་པོ་ཡོད་པ་ཡིན། སྔར་
ང་ཅག་གི་ཞབས་འབྲིང་དུ་ཆོས་བྱས་ཏེ་དགྲ་བཅོམ་པ་བློ་གྲོས་སོགས།
དགྲ་བཅོམ་པ་བརྒྱ་ཕྲག་གཅིག་ཙམ། ཆབ་མདོ་འཕགས་པ་ལ་སོགས་
པ་རང་ཕྱོགས་ཀྱི་བླ་ཆེན་ཞལ་བཞུགས་པ་མང་རབ་ཡོད་པས། སྤོན་སྐྱོ་
བ་མང་པོའི་འཕེན་ཤུགས་དང་མོས་སོགས་ཡོང་བ་ཡིན། འོན་ཀྱང་གི
སར་རྒྱལ་པོའི་སྐྱུང་དང་ཆ་འདྲ་བ་འདི་སྐྱིལ་མ་འཕེན་པ་དང་འདྲ་བ་ཞིག
ཀྱང་བས། འདིར་བཞུགས་རྣམས་ལ་གླེང་མོ་ཙམ་བྱས་པ་ཡིན། ཧློན་པོ་
ཏི་ཤུའི་སྐྱེ་བ་དཔྲའི་སྡེ་སྲིད་འདི་ཉིད་ང་ཅག་ལ་དད་པ་སྙད་ཅིག་ཀྱང་
སྐྱེ་བའི་སྐབས་མི་ཡོང་། འོན་ཀྱང་སྐྱོན་མི་འཛུག་གོ་ཨྠི། ཅེས་བཀའ་
ཨཱ་ལ་ཏོ། །དེར་ཚོགས་རྣམས་ཀྱི་ཕྱག་ཕུལ། ལེགས་སོ་བརྗོད། འདི་
རིགས་ཟིན་བྲིས་ཤོག་བུར་ཕབ་པོ། །ཀུན་ལ་མ་གསུང་ཞིག །ཕྱིར་ན་སྡེ་
སྲིད་ཚ་བས་སླན་ལ་ལྡོད་ན་མི་ལེགས། སྔོས་སུ་སྐལ་མེད་རྣམས་ལ་
བསྟན་ན་ཕལ་པའི་བློ་ལ་མི་ཤོང་བས་ངན་སོང་དུ་འགྲོ་བའི་རྒྱུ་དང་། རང་
ཉིད་སློབ་མ་ཁན་ཀྱང་སྡིག་ཆེན་དང་ སྲུང་མའི་འཚུབ་འཛིའི་ཉེན་པས་དད་
ལྡན་ཕན་ཚུན་ལས་གཞན་ལ་གསང་བའོ། །འགྲོ་འདྲེན་དམ་པ་འདིའི་མཛད་
པ་དང་ལྡན་རྣམས་ཀྱི་དོན་དུ་བཀོད་པ་འདིས་ཀྱང་ཕྱོགས་དུས་ཀུན་ཏུ

༄༅། །རྒྱལ་བའི་བསྟན་པ་རིན་པོ་ཆེ་དར་ཞིང་རྒྱས་པར་གྱུར་
ཅིག ༔ །འགྲོ་བའི་འདྲེན་མཆོག་དོན་ཆེན་གྲུབ་པ་ཡང་། །རྣམ་གྲང་པར་དུ་
བསྐྲུན་དགེས་རིས་མེད་ཀྱི། །འགྲོ་རྣམས་བདེ་སྐྱིད་རྫོགས་ལྡན་ལ་སྤྱོད་
ཅིང་༔ ༔མཐར་ཐུག་བྱང་ཆེན་ས་ལ་འགོད་པར་ཤོག །

།། སརྦ་མངྒ་ལཾ།། བཀྲ་ཤིས་ཤོག །

BIBLIOGRAPHY & NOTES

Lines inadvertently omitted by the copyist are reproduced at the bottom of pages f 35, f 45, and f 54, a small swastika symbol indicating the point of insertion into the text.

SHORT BIBLIOGRAPHY

Bacot, J., F. W. Thomas, and G. -Ch. Toussaint. *Documents de Touen-Houang relatifs à l'histoire du Tibet.* Paris: Librairie Orientaliste, Paul Geuthner, 1940-46.

Das, Sarat Chandra. *A Tibetan-English Dictionary.* Calcutta: The Bengal Secretariat Book Depot, 1902.

dGe SHes CHos Kyi Grags Pa. *brTSams Pai brDA Dag Ming TSHig gSal Ba bZHugs So: Tsang Wen Tz'u Tien* (Tibetan–Tibetan-Chinese Dictionary). Peking: Ming Tsu Ch'uh Pan Ch'u, 1957.

Duncan, M. H. *Harvest Festival Dramas of Tibet.* Hong Kong: Published by author, 1955.

Ekvall, Robert B. "Significance of Thirteen as a Symbolic Number in Tibetan and Mongolian Cultures." Journal American Oriental Society, LXXIX, 3 (1959), 188-192.

________. *Tibetan Skylines.* New York: Farrar, Straus & Young, 1952.

gZhon Nu dPal. *Deb THer sNGon Po.* Translated by G. N. Roerich as *The Blue Annals.* Calcutta: Royal Asiatic Society of Bengal, 1949 (Part I), 1953 (Part II).

Hoffman, Helmut. *Quellen zur Geschichte du tibetischen Bon-Religion.* Wiesbaden, F. Steiner, 1950.

Jäschke, Heinrich. *A Tibetan-English Dictionary.* London: Routledge & K. Paul, 1949.

Nebesky-Wojkowitz, René de. *Oracles and Demons of Tibet.* The Hague: Mouton & Co., 1956.

Pallis, Marco. *Peaks and Lamas.* New York: Alfred A. Knopf, Inc., 1946.

Petech, Luciano. *China and Tibet in the Early 18th Century.* Leiden: E. J. Brill, 1950.

Stein, Rolf. *L'épopée Tibetaine de Gesar.* Paris: Presses Universitaires de France, 1956.

Sum Pa mKHan Po. *dPag bSam lJon bZang.* Lokesh Chandra, ed. New Delhi: International Academy of Indian Culture, 1959.

Tucci, Giuseppe. *Tibetan Painted Scrolls.* Rome: Libreria della Stato, 1949.

Waddell, L. A. *The Buddhism of Tibet or Lamaism.* London: W. H. Allen & Co., 1895.

Woolf, H. I. *Three Tibetan Mysteries.* London: G. Routledge & Sons, 1924.

NOTES

1. The Tibetan calendar is divided into sixty-year cycles, each year of the cycle named for some set combination of five elements and twelve animals. For example, 1967 is Fire Sheep Year: 1968, Earth Ape Year; 1969, Earth Bird Year. The element which is the first part of the year name is male the first year it appears and female the second; thus 1968 is Earth Male Ape Year, 1969 Earth Female Bird Year. The Wood Male Tiger Year of the story was 1674.

Sa Ga is the fourth month of the year. The days of the lunar month are counted "upward" from the first to the fifteenth day, and "downward" from the fifteenth to the end. The high day is thus the fifteenth.

2. The second Panchen Lama, *Blo bZang Ye SHes* (1663-1737), is here stated to be the original narrator of this story. He is the "emanation-body," popularly called "reincarnation," of the first Panchen Lama. Emanation-body is similar to reincarnation except that a soul of the emanation-body hierarchy (a hierarchy founded by the Dalai Lama or the Panchen Lama), because he has attained enlightenment, has chosen the body he now inhabits. In a reincarnation hierarchy, on the other hand, the new form of the soul is determined by the good and evil acts in the previous lifetime.

3. The Great Wizard, *sNGags CHen,* is the title of the abbot of the *sNGags* (Wizard) college of the *bKra SHis lHun Po* (Heaped-up Good Fortune) monastery, the home monastery of the Panchen Lamas.

4. The term here rendered "official-pupil," *dPon Slob,* is an instance of the use of binoms, compound collective nouns, which are very common in the Tibetan language and which express the title of not one man but two. The term here designates two interlocutors, who state a common grievance, ask to hear the story, and then question in common its application to the situation. Other examples of binoms are father-son, father-mother, and official-servant.

5. *dByings Sa,* literally "high place," is an oblique reference to someone in the Dalai Lama's entourage who apparently had much power and whom it was considered inexpedient to name.

6. The phrase "lotus feet remain firm" is an honorific for not being dead.

7. "The Victorious One," which is the title of the Dalai Lama, is here placed after "The All-Knowing One," who is the Panchen. The two are linked in the compound father-son, and the relationship which the term describes is the politico-religious theme of the story.

8. *Kun bZang Ma* (All Good Female One) is a commonly used and popular Tibetan name. With the exception of the female diviner, all the female characters in the story have Tibetan names. This tale is considered to be one of the stories of the Buddha births, and so is presumably Indic in origin. But if the names have any significance, the core of the story is Tibetan, three of the four principal male characters and all three queens in the story have Tibetan names.

9. The Nagas, *Klu,* are the spirits who dwell under the earth, serpent spirits; their special domain is water—springs, rivers, and lakes. The land-owners, or soil-owners, are gods of the earth, who are said to protect their ground with great tyranny and jealousy.

10. Rare Perfection is the closest literal rending of the words *dKon* (rare, scarce) and *mCHog* (perfect, the best). It designates the highest concept of Buddhism, which is generally translated into English as "Jewel." Tibetan has at least two words for jewel: the use of either is in this connection inappropriate. The Tibetan scholars here consulted were shocked to know that that concept toward which their deepest adoration turns is called "Jewel," and they felt that the concept is lowered in value if it is linked to a material object. Indeed, from the manner in which *dKon mCHog* is used in common parlance—"*dKon mCHog* knows" and "pray to *dKon mCHog*"—a fair case can be made for the Das and Jaschke dictionaries' use of "God" as an equivalent for the term, although such use violates Buddhist doctrine.

11. The god *TSa Muntri* is evidently of Indic origin. There is a similar Tibetan term, but it is used for a subclass of "the arrogant" gods. (Nebesky-Wojkowitz, p. 271)

12. The word "oblation" is used for the Tibetan *gTor Ma* (the broken-up), which is the term for a particular category of offerings, which consists of figures and symbolically shaped objects made from dough, butter, etc. They differ from the more general *mCHod Pa* (offerings) in that, typically, they are broken up and scattered or burned.

13. The aboriginal beings were the original, pre-Buddhist gods of Tibet, who were subdued by the great thaumaturge *Slob dPon Rin Po CHe* and converted into the protectors of religion.

14. *AH TSa Ra,* from the Indic term *Atsara,* refers to a wandering ascetic.

15. *sPyan Ras gZigs* (Viewing Eye) and *aJam dPal* (Mild Glory) are what Jaschke calls "the two great half-divine Bodhisattvas of the Northern Buddhists." They are here, at the beginning of the story, placed in a sons and father relationship to Lord *Od dPag Med* (Light Unmeasured). *sPyan Ras gZigs* is the nationally recognized guardian spirit of Tibet; he is believed to have been emanated in the ape who is the mythological father of the Tibetan race, in *Srong bTSan sGam Po,* the most famous of the Tibetan kings, who officially brought Buddhism to Tibet, and in the successive Dalai Lamas. *aJam dPal* is believed to have been emanated in the Tibetan scholar who brought a system of writing to Tibet, *THomi Sambhota;* in the Tibetan King *KHri Srong lDe bTSan,* the patron of *Slob dPon Rin Po CHe*; and later in the Manchu emperors of China. Lord *Od dPag Med,* who is emanated as the Panchen Lamas, is here stated to be the spiritual father of the two.

16. The Tibetan *Dus bZang* (good times or days) are the particularly auspicious days of the lunar month. They are said to be the 8th, 10th, 15th, 25th, and, whenever the lunar month has thirty days, the 30th.

17. The *mTSHan mKHan* (sign one), or "sign-discerning one," is the soothsayer who notes all the marks and characteristics of a newborn child and the associated astrological factors, and suggests a suitable name. The term *mTSHan* (sign) is also the honorific for the word "name."

18. "Place of a king" is the most appropriate translation here for *rGyal Sa,* (which sometimes has to be translated as realm or country), for it reflects some of the folk-language nuance of the colloquial Tibetan of the story, and avoids the loaded inferences of "succeed to the throne" or "take over the position of the king."

19. *Don THams aGrub Pa,* the Fulfiller of All Meaning, also defined as the "Fulfillment of Every Wish," is considered to belong by right to Buddha himself. In its shortened form, *Don aGrub* (Meaning Fulfillment), it is a name of the historic Buddha and is also a common Tibetan name.

20. The "six letters" are the six syllables *OHm Ma Ni Pad Me Hum,* the basic prayer formula of Tibetan Buddhism, which is universally used. Its authorship is traditionally ascribed to King *Srong bTSan sGam Po,* the patron saint of Tibet. Frequently translated "Hail the jewel in the lotus," its real meaning is esoterically obscure. The only syllables which have been semantically identified are *Pad Me,* Lotus, and these are borrowed from Sanskrit.

21. "Unworthy" here means that *Padma Can* (Lotus Possessing) was a commoner. Faults do appear in her character, but the basis of the charge was that she was not the daughter of a king. Evidently what was first intended as a liaison with no thought of marriage became tacitly regularized when the girl announced she was pregnant. The announcement itself in its enumeration of omens and signs is carefully modeled after the one which had told of the coming of sons.

22. *Byang CHub Sems dPaa,* here anglicized for convenience as CHANG CHUB SEMPA, means "Pure Hero-mind," which is heroic in that it is permeated with Buddahood, incapable of self-interest but concerned only with the welfare of all others. This concept has often been translated with the Sanskrit "Boddhisattva," a word foreign to the Tibetan understanding of it.

23. *Don Yod* (Have Meaning), the name of the younger brother, is also a common Tibetan name, although not as frequently encountered as *Don aGrub.* Although most Tibetans, even the very unlearned, associate the name *Don aGrub* with the historic Buddha, very few think of *Don Yod* as anything but an ordinary name, and it has no recognized significance comparable to that of CHANG CHUB SEMPA as an emanation of the Buddhahood. In the story, however, the signs which follow the naming immediately identify him as an emanation. Only later in the tale is *Don Yod* identified with a specific emanation.

24. In this statement and all the discussions that follow concerning the eligibility of the two princes, the argument shifts between the claims of primogeniture and the matter of pure and less pure royal blood. Neither concept is truly native to Tibetan society, and in Tibetan history both are as honored in the

breach as in the observance. The popular sympathy for the younger brother, which has been discussed in the introduction, reflects in this case a conscious or unconscious rejection of both concepts.

25. The Tibetan phrase *PHyag* or *Lag* (hand) *rTen* (base or representation) is the gift which is passed from hand to hand. It may be only part of the many items of a great *aBul Ba* (gift), but symbolically it is the most important part. When people meet their "hands must not be empty," hence the widespread use of the *KHa bTags,* the ceremonial scarf which is given at any meeting. This scarf takes the place of a hand-gift or accompanies it.

26. In Tibetan "himself," "ourselves," "myself" may be added after the corresponding pronouns to emphasize them.

27. The apparent need for popular acclaim and endorsement by the nobles and ministers with regard to the succession to the throne is further indication that neither blue blood nor the right of the first born automatically ensured the succession.

28. The *Sug Pa* herb is used as a substitute for soap, and with it one may work up somewhat of a lather.

29. The word *rTen,* which has been translated here as "shrine," may also be translated "base," "receptacle," or "representation." It is ideally and typically tripartite. This is true whether the shrine is a great structure among monastery or palace buildings, or whether it is the humblest miniature belonging to a poor family. To be a "body, word, mind" shrine it must contain an image of Buddha as the symbol of body, some printed or written portion of the scriptures as the symbol of word, and one or all of the following as the symbol of mind: a stupa in miniature, a ritual thunderbolt, a ritual bell.

30. *rGyal Pos sMra Ba Lan gCig* (The king speaks once) is a popular Tibetan aphorism. In harmony with the idea developed in the text, the implication is that once the king has spoken there can be no disagreement with what has been said and that even he cannot change it.

31. The suggestion of the queen, which had been rashly and inadvertently accepted by the king, was that the prince should be exiled. She did not suggest that he should be drowned. But the prince evidently felt that the exigencies of the journey would be made the excuse for drowning him. This suspicion is accepted by Tibetans as being well-founded.

32. Thirteen years of age is a symbolic age frequently appearing in Tibetan history and folklore. Many of the legendary kings of Tibet are said to have succeeded to royal power at that age, and it is also the age at which the religious leader who systematized the Bon doctrines is said to have received daemonic inspiration. (Ekvall, "Significance of Thirteen . . ."; Hoffman, p. 211)

33. The names assigned to the "two pious ministers" of what is specifically stated to be the Indian king of an Indian country point up the need, apparently felt by the original narrator of the story, to invoke all the sacrosanct associations of India but yet create a preponderantly Tibetan tale, in dramatis personae, interest, and final significance or application. One name, *Rab brTan* (Superior Firmness), is a common Tibetan name, and the other, *Dzaya Dhara,* is typically Indic in origin and association.

34. The translation of the word *sMon Lam* (wish way) is possibly best solved

by the use of the compound "wish-prayer." It has been variously rendered as "wishing prayer," "prayer," etc. The native Tibetan scholars here consulted argued strongly for the connotation "wish" without realizing how weak the English word is in comparison to the Tibetan concept. The Tibetan view of existence accepts the world of phenomena as coexistent with the world of thought and even with the world of imagination. In that world a "wish" is something of power which when "sown"—the commonest verb used with *sMon Lam*—produces the harvest of a caused result.

35. Buddhist doctrine divides living creatures into six categories: the gods, demi-gods, human beings, animals, beings in hell, and hunger demons.

36. *CHos NYid* is here translated as "natural law" because in this connotation *CHos* is not the religion of Buddhism or even religion in its widest application, but refers to the law, or laws, of existence—the "eternal fitness of things."

37. The *dPag TSHad* (proportion measured), here translated "league," is a unit of linear measurement which was imported along with writing, religion, etc., from India.

38. The incongruities which develop when an attempt is made to combine Indic story forms and environmental factors with Tibetan ones, are brought into sharp relief by the use of the words *Byang THang* (north plain) as the designation of the area to which the princes flee. In Tibet the *Byang THang* is not just a northern plain but is the proper name of the high north-central plateau—which is largely uninhabited because of altitude. This region is indeed pathless and occasionally sandy, as here stated, but nowhere are there forests, fruit trees, and areas suitable for cultivation. Although beasts of prey are found, there are no monkeys or—excepting the partridge—such birds as later appear in the story. All the later events belong to some Indian northern plain and not to the *Byang THang* of Tibet.

39. The Tibetan term *Ri Glang Po Chei sNa aDra* (hill like an elephant's nose) is the description of the shape of a hill. It is not to be confused with the Tibetan term *Ri sNa* (hill nose), p. 29, which means "spur," "shoulder," and "brow" of a hill.

40. Probably the parrot, for it is said to be able to learn human speech.

41. A sparrow—the common Tibetan name is *KHang Byiu* (house little bird). Considered an augury.

42. The cuckoo is sometimes also called the Turquoise bird. It is well known and highly lauded in mythology and is valued as an augury of good fortune. (Stein, p. 192)

43. This part of the wish-prayer of Prince *Don aGrub* is part of the build-up of the Panchen's position, the main theme of the tale. Here the prince, who has already been identified as the emanation of the patron saint of Tibet—one with the emanation ancestor of the Tibetan people, the first Buddhist king, and the Dalai Lamas—is represented as bewailing the lack of a savior lama to rescue him and his brother. The prayer implied in this statement of regret is answered later.

44. The Tibetan term *Ting NGe aDZin* is the technical term for both a posture and a mental state commonly known by the Sanskrit word *Samadhi*—a state in meditation of psychic realization. (Jaschke)

45. Macaques and Langurs are monkeys native to Tibet. Both are here as-

signed pious roles befitting their popular image. The Tibetan word for macaque, *sPreu,* is the term for *sPreu Byang CHub Sems dPaa* (monkey pure hero-mind), the mythological CHANG CHUB SEMPA, ancestor of the Tibetan race.

46. The tiger is one of the most important creatures of Tibetan mythology. To it are ascribed great strength and arrogant fearlessness. As a symbolic creature it is oddly ambivalent, appearing in both benevolent and malevolent roles. Here the tiger appears as the spokesman of the lurking cynicism and scepticism of which most Tibetans have at least a trace. It is not one of the allegorical creatures of the story, for it is not identified at the conclusion of the tale as a historical figure. Perhaps the narrator himself, the Panchen Lama, used this device to express some of his own feelings about his rival emanations.

47. The phrase "box of slate slabs" has been used for the Tibetan *gYam sGrom.* It is not really a stone coffin but a makeshift, protective structure such as Tibetan hunters use when they wish to protect the carcass of any game they have killed, building around and over it a covering of stone or, when they can find them, stone slabs.

48. In any Tibetan enumeration of wild animals, *Ri Dwags* (game animals) or the ruminants—wild yak, sheep, deer, etc.—are always distinguished from the *gCan gZan* (beasts of prey)—wolves, leopards, bears, etc.

49. *Grong* (village) and *aBrog* (wilderness suited for pasturage) in the Tibetan text probably stand for *Grong Pa* (village ones) and *aBrog Pa* (wilderness ones). The former term is one of three definitive terms for sedentary agriculturalists, and the latter, the universally used term for pastoral nomads.

50. The person introduced in this modest and casual manner is the lama mentioned at the very beginning of the story. In self-deprecatory style he later says of himself, "I am aged and somewhat infirm." He is, however, the prototype of the Panchen Lama and, as he befriends and instructs the prince, is successively revealed as the spiritual "father" to the prince "son"; as the one coming from the breast of *Od dPag Med* from the Buddhafield—or the Buddhahood—and the heaven of bliss; as *Od dPag Med* his very self who is also said to be *Ye SHes Od Mi aGyur Ba* (Intuitive Wisdom Unchanging Light); as the one who consults the stars, converts and ordains kings, founds and names monasteries, foretells the progress of religion in Tibet and eventually, after having maintained his role as hero protagonist of the good against the villain of the story, signalizes the elimination of the latter in a landslide. At the end of the tale, the narrator, the Panchen Lama, flatly states that he himself is the "excellent lama of that time"—the benefactor, tutor, and spiritual father of the prince who is the Dalai Lama and the emanation of *sPyan Ras gZigs.*

51. The three lineage lords are later called the sons of *Od dPag Med* and are identified as *sPyan Ras gZigs* (Viewing Eye), *aJam dByangs* (Mild Melody)—another name for *aJam dPal* (Mild Glory)—and *mTHu CHen THob Pa* (To Obtain Great Might), which is another name for *PHyag Na rDo rJe* (Thunderbolt at Hand). The three lords are thought to correspond to the recurring triad of the body, word, and mind.

52. The theme of perfect, unquestioning obedience to parental authority, here called "sublime behavior," even when that authority is exercised in an arbitrary

and unjust manner, is one of the many themes of this story. This is very much an Indian ideal, and appears in greater perfection in the *Visvantara*—in Tibetan, *Dri Med Kun lDan* (Without Taint Endowed with All)—the most famous of the birth stories of the Buddha and one which is almost purely Indic in themes and incidents. But *The Younger Brother Don Yod* is a greater mixture of Indic and Tibetan material, and although the words "without taint" appear as a characterization of the hero, his obedience is not perfect. At the very start he takes flight instead of awaiting formal exile, and once, in a proverb, he speaks with clear bitterness about his plight, "I am like a hair pulled from the butter" to describe his feeling of being rejected and thrown away.

53. This apparition is a dramatic figure and not a specific member of the Tibetan pantheon. He gives himself the name *Beg TSi,* a word generally thought to be borrowed from the Mongolian and meaning "the one wearing mail." By his promise to become a protector of the lama and prince, he foreshadows the conversion of all varieties of local deities into the *Srung Ma* (Protector Ones), who are such an important part of Tibetan Buddhism. (Tucci, p. 595)

54. The idea of poisonous snakes is certainly Indian, for it is doubtful whether there are any poisonous snakes in Tibet proper. They are here given a malevolent role.

55. Jaschke (p. 400) suggests "wild rice" for the term *aBras Sa Lu.* However, it refers to the original and first wild grain used as food by early mankind and is not necessarily rice.

56. The literal meaning of the word *aGro Ba,* translated as "creatures," is "goers." The Tibetan language is rich in a long series of terms and phrases based on the concept of going as the essential aspect of being.

57. The literal translation of the term *Byin Rlabs* is "bestowal wave," which shows the basic meaning of the Tibetan more closely than the word "blessing."

58. These are the *SHang SHang,* defined as "a fabulous creature having wings and bird's feet but otherwise like a human being." (Jaschke, p. 556)

59. Partridges, to a greater extent than most other birds, are hated and feared by the Tibetans as an omen of bad luck. When encountered on a journey, they presage a meeting with robbers; they are a sign of want and starvation. Here the partridge is given a malevolent role and later is identified as a malicious mischief-maker, a monk who sows dissension between the second Panchen Lama and the fifth Dalai Lama.

60. "The sound of the dragon" is the common term for thunder, which is supposed to come from the dragon in the sky. Thus the fame of the prince is "thunderous loud."

61. *PHyag rDor* is a contraction of *Phyag Na rDo rJe* (Thunderbolt At Hand). See note no. 51.

62. Both the diviners mentioned in the story are female. The one first mentioned was rewarded by being made a minister. Although the official oracles of Tibet are now mostly men, it is popularly thought that the earliest and best of the diviners were female. Many elderly women are credited with having great clairvoyance, although doctrinally this is an attribute of a CHANG CHUB SEMPA.

63. Of the eight great Nagas known to the Tibetan public, the first two here named, who are called kings, are the best known, although there are prayers and ritual for all of them, and numerous legends and histories relating to them. Illustrative of the Tibetan and Indian influences throughout this story, four of the seven have Tibetan names and the others, Sanskrit ones.

64. The term here translated "fated" is *Las Kyi* (of the deeds); but its meaning is the determining power of the deeds in a previous existence—what is often called karma—on the character and condition of present existence. It is thus that the villain of the play is introduced. He is immediately painted a deep black, insane with the three poisons of lustfulness, wrathfulness, and stupidity, a doubter of the truth and a delighter in edged weapons. He remains throughout the play the implacable antagonist of the lama, and his hatred extends to the two brothers on every occasion.

65. The Tibetan verb here means "to sell," and the figure of speech refers to the finality of the last offer made by a determined bargainer—"take it or leave it."

66. The word "threaten" means any degree of menacing, from the simple twisting of a sword handle preparatory to drawing the blade from the sheath—a very common gesture in any Tibetan dispute—to raising it to strike or thrust, to pricking the skin or striking with the flat of the blade. The minister has already been characterized as one who likes to carry a cutting weapon.

67. The Tibetan phrase is literally "mind slipping away to the prince," but "mind" here means the affections which in English common usage are "heart."

68. *rGya mTSHoi Dus Ran* (set time of the great sea) is a contraction which summarizes all the causes and events of the making of a sacrifice to the lake. *rGya mTSHo* (great sea), which usually is taken to mean the ocean, is a disproportionate term for a lake the circumference of which is said to be only six leagues. But the story assumes that the lake is little more than an entrance to the submarine world which is linked with all the oceans: the entire *Klui Yul* (country of the Nagas) where all the kings and millions of Nagas assemble.

69. The phrase "counting as men count" is based on the fact that in the submarine world of the Nagas there is neither sun nor moon and thus no way of counting days or months (moons).

70. The *sNum* (grease) is not oil, but in this case the grease rising to the surface of the stew of dried meat. There is much action packed into the terse sentences of this scene which in the play is acted out in much detail.

71. The Tibetan title *Rin Po CHe,* commonly written *Rimpoche,* which is consistently applied to high ecclesiastics, has the literal meaning shown here.

72. In this instance "elephant's nose" refers to an elephant nose projection, an ornamental feature of the architecture of the palace.

73. In this case the predetermining power of previous works, making for karma, is attributed to the agency of wish-prayers. See notes 34, 64.

74. Becoming *Yab Yum* (father-mother) means marriage and is also a euphemism for the consummation of marriage. The gods and their female consorts in sexual embrace are called the *Yab Yum*.

75. The term *PHa sPad* is a colloquial and slightly derogatory form of the

more common binom *PHa Bu* (father-son) of the honorific form *Yab Sras* (father-son) which appears frequently in the narrative.

76. The gems of wish fulfillment are a class of objects whose form and material characteristics are not specified. Possession of one of such objects makes fulfillment of wishes possible, hence its high value, and the ascription "gem." The Sanskrit term is *cintamani.*

77. The *Rin Po CHe sNa bDun* (seven items of great value) refers to the following seven precious things: gold, silver, coral, pearl, lapis lazuli, opal, and either crystal or jasper.

78. The eight emblems of good fortune—also called the "eight glorious emblems"—are the golden fish, the umbrella, the left-spiralled conch shell, the lucky diagram, the victorious banner, the vase, the lotus, and the wheel.

79. *ZHabs sPyi Bor Blans So* (to put the foot on the crown of the head) is the sign of deepest homage. The father-king is speaking to the elder brother, but from the events of the immediate future when the younger brother takes his father's place, it seems safe to assume that the "foot-on-crown" act of homage involved the younger brother as well, and the king and queen were downgraded in relation to both their sons—a Tibetan but not an Indian behavior pattern.

80. Polyandrous marriage, previously implied when the binom "father-mother" was qualified by the phrase "the three" (p. 53), is here made explicit and given social sanction at the highest, royal level. The nature of the story, with its great religious, allegorical involvement and doctrinal emphasis, also makes this sanction a religious one of great significance in the prototype of the Dalai Lama himself. This arrangement, in which the woman is first the wife of the elder brother and then the younger brother becomes co-husband, is the typical form of polyandry now practiced among Tibetans. Although sometimes two—and occasionally more—brothers become co-husbands at the time of marriage, the more usual development is that the younger brother or brothers are admitted to conjugal privileges as they reach maturity. In the story the two brothers rule over separate and reputedly Indic kingdoms; but in addition to having Tibetan names and associations, they have a wife in common, who also has a Tibetan name. This polyandrous situation is strongly atypical in the Indic tradition.

81. The Lama *Legs Pa Blo Gros* is here given pre-eminence in the seating arrangements, which pre-figures the importance the narrator arrogates to himself, the Panchen Lama.

82. The law of causality is here the moral law of reward and retribution—good follows from good, evil from evil.

83. This prophecy points to the reign of *Srong bTSan sGam Po* in the early or middle seventh century.

84. The lama of the story is said to have become the CHANG CHUB SEMPA *Dibam Gara,* who appeared in India. He then became an abbot of the Tibetans (*KHa Ba Can),* was known as *Atisha* and was often called *Jo Bo* (The Lord).

85. The *Dzaya* here mentioned was the best one of Atisha's disciples.

86. Attention is here focused on the younger brother, *Prajana,* whose Tibetan name was *SHes Rab rDo rJe,* and who was a famous disciple of *Dzaya;* but here he is said to belong to, i.e., was in the spiritual lineage of, *Don Yod.* The roles of the younger brother are given a marked importance: he becomes one of great doctrinal achievement, a royal sponsor, and he is later linked with the emanation of the lama, the Lord *Od dPag Med.* Much more is said about him than about his elder brother, and the obvious intention is to associate him and the lama as important agents of the doctrine in the developments foretold here and on the next page. The Panchen Lama here links the fortunes of the popular younger brother with his own, to the implied exclusion of the Dalai Lama.

87. The *Yab Yum* (father-mother) manner here refers to the married clergy or famous and pious laymen who were married.

88. The prohibition against casual and indiscriminate revelation of the story is couched in the form of a solemn warning of damnation. It is an overall warning, possibly applicable to the process of publication. In such a frame of reference it is a story which was not intended for non-believers. The warning, later repeated, also had an immediate application at the time it was told. It was a piece of politico-religious propaganda directed against powerful factions and persons, and its primary distribution was to be limited to those belonging to the party and faction of the Panchen Lama.

89. This is *NGag dBang Blo bZang rGya mTSHo* (1617-1682). Often called the Great Fifth, he unified Tibet and established the tradition of direct and effective rule by the Dalai Lamas. (Waddell, pp. 35, 233)

90. This identification of the lama of the story and the Panchen Lama was stated at the beginning of the story and thereafter frequently suggested.

91. As of the date (1674) when the story is told, the former prime minister was *PHring Las rGya mTSHo* (1660-1668).

92. The prime minister of that date and the one who throughout the allegory is figured as the villain, was *Blo bZang mTHu sTobs,* who had been made prime minister in 1669. It is not clear why he was so much disliked by the Panchen Lama. Because he had occasioned scandal, he was retired late in 1675. (Petech, p. 379; *Sum Pa mKHan Po,* p. 72)

93. The mother probably refers to the Panchen's own mother; otherwise there would be further identification.

94. Of the snakes, one or two are located within the retinue of the Panchen Lama and the others are in the administrative organization—the peak and base —of the Dalai Lama.

95. From here on the text has the appearance of an afterthought. The warning itself seems repetitious. A number of the identifications are suggestive and qualified rather than certain. An identification is made which is ex post facto to the conditions of the time when the story was told. *AH Bar,* who most certainly is *AH Bar Sang rGyas rGya mTSHo,* is called the prime minister. At that time, however, he was just eleven years old, and he only became prime minister in 1679. Comment concerning the villain of the story, *Trishu* the prime minister, while it maintains the evil of his role, is relaxed in tone and ends with the assurance that no harm is done. This comforting assurance may have been based on ex post facto knowledge that he had been disgraced and removed in 1675, a

year after the telling of the story. Thus there are fairly strong indications that this latter portion of the text is an editorial addition to the original, (Petech, pp. 378-380; *Sum Pa mKHan Po,* p. 73)

96. The *De Mo Rin Po CHe* is a well-known emanation-body lama in Lhasa. He now is one of the four *rGyal TSHab* (king representative) of the Dalai Lama. What his office was at that time is not known.

97. This is one of the interlocutors identified in note no. 3.

98. Neither *Blo bZang Byams Pa* nor *Blo bZang Nor Bu* can be identified other than by the manner in which they are mentioned, which suggests that they were pretty well known and presumably among the retainers of the Panchen; particularly since *rJe Drung* (Lord Near), which precedes one of the names, is the title of a courtier.

99. A "treasure prophecies one" is someone who reveals and takes out cached treasurers, which may be either ritual objects or writings allegedly hidden in former times. *Padma Sambhava* is supposed to have hidden many such treasures throughout Tibet. The identity of the revealer here is not known, but, from the context, he too was a familiar member of the entourage of the Panchen Lama.

100. This treasurer was probably the Panchen's own treasurer.

101. *sByin Pa* is without doubt *Blo bZang sByin Pa,* who was manager of the *rNam rGyal* college of the Potala until 1675, when he was made prime minister. (Petech, p. 379)

102. *bKaa Blon* (word or order minister) is the title of a member of the cabinet of the Dalai Lama—and thus a high official of the central government.

103. *ZHal sNa Nas* (From The Presence) is an honorific form of address for important emanation lamas. *mNGaa Rigs* as a name means nothing but if, as is possible, *Rigs* is a mistake for *Ris,* then this refers to the *mNGaa Ris* lama in western Tibet. His present emanation body is the younger brother of the Dalai Lama.

104. *bsTan aDZin CHos rGyal* is the Tibetan name for Gushri Khan, the Mongolian Khan from Koko Nor, who, after conquering Tibet in 1642, bestowed temporal power to rule it on the Fifth Dalai Lama.

105. This is one of the abbots. His identification is not known, but from the context he is probably someone placed in power by Gushri Khan himself.

106. The *ZHabs Drung* (at the foot of) of the *gYon Ru* (left division or banner) is taken to be some lama appointee of the Mongol Khan, wielding power over the left banner of the Mongol organization of Tibet.

107. This would be the abbot of the great monastery of *dGe lDan*. The name *Gling Yag Pa* (Good Park One) is probably a designation of origin rather than a personal name.

108. Although in the text one of the winged creatures is identified as *Bog rDo,* a Chinese, the name certainly has a Mongolian sound—like the Mongol equivalent of *Rin Po CHe* which is the title of high emanation lamas. The second creature of the pair is said to be the king of those *Hor*. This word at various periods in Tibetan history has been used to designate Mongols and other, possibly Turanian, peoples within and on the borders of Tibet. It certainly means Mongol and may designate the Dzungars.

109. This is a somewhat general summary of those on the side of the Panchen Lama. *CHab mDo PHags Pa La* is an emanation lineage—which has continued to the present—of Chamdo in eastern Tibet.

110. This is a Sanskrit phrase which Tibetans interpret as meaning "Good fortune to all."

111. This last word of the play again points up the importance the Tibetans assign to "going" as the substitute for, or manifestation of, "being." Instead of saying "Let good fortune be," Tibetans shout for the arrival of blessing with the words "Let good fortune come."